S0-BSR-575

Acknowledgements

Completing this book required a collaborative and
resourceful team effort. I would like to thank Frank
Luby at Present Tense LLC who helped organize
and shape my ideas into a cohesive manuscript.

I would also like to thank Ben Christensen, Gregory
Dietz, John Baxter, Sandra Moerch, Anita Varshney,
and Ana Apostolovska of the SAP Next-Gen team
for their creative inputs and strong support.

Thanks also to Sissel Hansen and her team at Startup
Guide for outstanding support in publishing the book.

Ann Rosenberg
New York, New York
January 2019

Author **Ann Rosenberg** is a tech executive, futurist and purpose driven innovation thought leader, as well as blockchain expert and UN Women GICC member and program lead for **#sheinnovates**.

She is Senior Vice President & Global Head of SAP Next-Gen, a Purpose Driven Innovation University and Community aligned with SAP's commitment to the 17 UN Global Goals for sustainable development and supporting SAP's 413,000+ customers across 25 industries and 7 lines-of-business in more than 180 countries. The community leverages more than 3,700 educational institutions in 117 countries, over 150 SAP Next-Gen labs/hubs at universities, more than 40 Girls' Lounges, more than 100 SAP Next-Gen Chapters, as well as startups, accelerators, tech community partners, venture firms, futurists, and purpose driven institutions.

"**Science Fiction – A Starship for Enterprise Innovation**" is an insightful and engaging look at what the author calls "**Innovation 4.0**". This next generation innovation methodology enables purpose driven innovators to unlock creativity and envision disruptive solutions that can accelerate achieving the 17 Sustainable Development Goals (SDGs).

"Innovation 4.0 is all about being inspired by science fiction while being guided by purpose aligned with the SDGs, to uncover bold, new models for using exponential technologies such as AI, machine learning, blockchain, and IoT to both profit and serve a higher social purpose," asserts author and purpose driven futurist **Ann Rosenberg**.

This book offers a path forward to enterprises unsure about how to respond to the unprecedented and unabated technological surge we are witnessing today. With science fiction's proven track record of predicting future technological developments, science fiction thinking can serve as a wellspring for disruptive innovation and for an enterprise's ongoing transformation into an intelligent enterprise.

Science Fiction - A Starship for Enterprise Innovation

Publisher: **Sissel Hansen**
Author: **Ann Rosenberg**

Authored by
the **SAP Next-Gen** program
10 Hudson Yards
New York, New York 10001

Printed in Berlin, Germany by
Medialis-Offsetdruck GmbH
Heidelbergerstraße 65, 12435 Berlin

Published by
Startup Guide World ApS
Kanonbådsvej 2, 1437 Copenhagen K
info@startupguide.com

Visit: **startupguide.com**

ISBN: **978-3-947624-16-4**

Science Fiction

A Starship for Enterprise Innovation

Ann Rosenberg

SAP next-**gen** ▶▶▏

Printed in

100% Recycled Paper
Circleoffset White Paper

CONTENTS

INTRODUCTION

The urgent case for science fiction thinking

Do you recall the first time you realized that something which made a difference in your life – no matter what phase of it – first appeared in a movie many years ago?

We'll share with you an obvious example. Pick up your smartphone, which we assume lies within arm's reach. Believe it or not, that handheld device – which we seemingly cannot live without – does not trace its roots back to the genius minds at Bell Labs or to visionary entrepreneurs pulling all-nighters in their garages. No, it traces its roots directly back to the 1960's television program *Star Trek*.

If that connection sounds too far-fetched, you could ask the mobile phone's inventor himself, Martin Cooper. When he was director of research and development at Motorola, he claimed that the *Star Trek* communicator inspired the design of the first mobile phone in the early 1970s.

> *"That was not fantasy to us,"* Cooper said.
> *"That was an objective."* [1]

Martin Cooper took his inspiration from science fiction to work with him. Far from being crazy or nerdy, this inspiration provided the focus and clarity of vision that helped him and his teams create a device that changed the world. The smartphone, the grandchild to Cooper's original cellular phone, is arguably the most rapidly dispersed technological product in human history.

We would like you to treat this book, *SAP Next-Gen Science Fiction Thinking* as your inspiration to do the same thing that Mr. Cooper did: bring your science fiction ideas and inspiration to work with you. This book will help you activate your latent science fiction passion and apply it to real business problems. We argue that science fiction thinking is rapidly becoming an essential ingredient in the innovation process. This makes it a source of true competitive advantage as intelligent enterprises seek exponential growth and innovation with purpose. Science fiction thinking also offers a path forward to enterprises unsure about how to respond to the unprecedented and unabated technological surge we are witnessing today.

Science fiction's proven track record is one reason we are confident that science fiction thinking can serve as a wellspring for disruptive innovation and for an enterprise's ongoing transformation into an intelligent enterprise. The cellphone, which now lives on as the smartphone, is only one of many compelling examples of science fiction-to-fact that you will experience throughout this book. The difference between those groundbreaking innovations and the ones that are making our lives better now and in the years to come is the process of their genesis, a process we call Innovation 4.0.

As illustrated in Figure 1, Innovation 4.0 is the latest stage in innovation which spans an era that began with Innovation 1.0, the rise of Silicon Valley. Innovation 2.0 followed as other regions around the world adopted the Silicon Valley model. From there, Innovation 3.0 followed as leading innovators began to link innovation to positive social outcomes aligned with accelerating the achievement of the 17 UN Sustainable Development Goals (SDGs). And today we are seeing the emergence of Innovation 4.0.

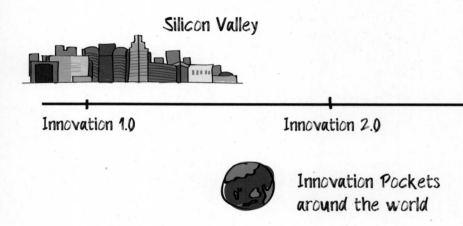

Innovation 4.0 is a next generation innovation methodology enabling purpose driven innovators to unlock creativity and envision disruptive solutions that can accelerate achieving the 17 Sustainable Development Goals (SDGs).

Innovation 4.0 is all about being inspired by science fiction while being guided by purpose aligned with the SDGs, to uncover bold, new models for using exponential technologies such as AI, machine learning, blockchain, and IoT to both profit and serve a higher social purpose.

The ideas of science fiction thinking and Innovation 4.0 may conjure up images of creative collaboration beyond the reach of most business people. But this book is not for the science fiction writers, illustrators, designers, futurists, and filmmakers who dazzle us with spectacular or scary future worlds. This book is for anyone who has ever thought *"wow, if only ..."* and let his or her imagination run wild. And we have all had those thoughts, haven't we?

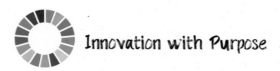

Innovation with Purpose

Innovation 3.0 ————————————————————————— **Innovation 4.0**

un global goals
for sustainable development

\+

science fiction
thinking

\+

exponential
technology

Figure 1: Innovation 1.0 to 4.0

What we were all missing, though, was a way to channel that passionate thinking into a business context. How can we transform *"wow, if only ..."* from silent thoughts in our private minds into the ideas which can drive our enterprises' next wave of innovation? How can we change the perception of "science fiction thinking" from crazy to comfortable, and make this powerful innovation tool the rule rather the exception? How can we infuse a "science fiction" mindset into an often risk-averse and conservative corporate world? Finally, how can we use this thinking to explore, understand, and reconcile the positive and negative sides of the daunting exponential technologies we now have at our fingertips?

This book will answer those questions for you. In doing so, it helps you open the doors and dissolve the barriers which are preventing you from viewing your current and especially your future business challenges through the science fiction lens. After all, coming up with the "crazy idea" is a talent we all have within us. Astro Teller, the head of X (formerly Google X) eloquently described this universal capability in an interview with *The Washington Post*: [2]

"Everyone is qualified to come up with ideas. If you go to a kindergarten and you ask kids to have some ideas, every single child in the room will have ideas for you. Crazy ideas. The ability for us to have ideas and to put them out in front of our peers is lost as we grow up. It's beaten out of us. It's not something that you need to find rarefied people who are good at doing it.

The trick is to make them feel safe, so that they can put their ideas in front of their peers and not feel like they're going to get laughed at. And then you have to weed through those ideas in a thoughtful way."

The success of Innovation 4.0 will depend on our ability to regain that appetite for the crazy idea and create the comfort level to let those ideas flow and receive their due consideration. Many ideas that were initially considered crazy have contributed to creating the world we now inhabit. The process of creating new and better worlds has never been easier, thanks to the technologies we now have available.

It's time to activate your inner science fiction imagination

"Science fiction isn't useful because it's predictive,"

writes author Eliot Peper in the Harvard Business Review.

"It's useful because it reframes our perspective on the world. Like international travel or meditation, it creates space for us to question our assumptions." [3]

Peper's article bears the title "Why Business Leaders Need to Read More Science Fiction." But science fiction plays a much more important and vital role in our lives than merely serving as the setting and plot driver for entertainment. For centuries, science fiction has served as humanity's crystal ball, with remarkable clarity and accuracy. Many of the products, services, or experiences first encountered in these fictional worlds are now so interwoven in our daily lives that we take them for granted and forget their origins.

The lure of science fiction, and its motivational abilities, is nothing new. In 1899, a 17-year-old boy in Massachusetts had read the recently-published *War of the Worlds*, a novel by H.G. Wells. The book, he would later say, "gripped my imagination tremendously." [4] He climbed a tree, looked into the night sky, and imagined a device which could bring mankind to the moon or Mars. That experience filled him "with a sense of purpose in life." [5] That boy would grow up to one day state that "[e]very vision is a joke until the first man accomplishes it." [6] He was Robert H. Goddard, the American scientist who built and launched the first liquid-fueled rocket in 1926 and is considered one of the fathers of modern rocketry.

Rocketry may not seem to be an important part of our day-to-day lives, but its legacy makes many of our day-to-day tasks possible. One aspect of modern life that goes unnoticed are the satellites which enable us to watch television, make international phone calls, and use GPS applications to figure out how to drive our cars from Point A to Point B in a strange city. Of course, each of those satellites entered orbit thanks to a rocket.

Just as importantly, science fiction also provides us with a fascinating lens to examine and understand complex problems. Comparisons to international travel, meditation, and mindfulness fit very well in this context. Decades ago, executives would rarely travel overseas. When they or their employees did happen to encounter other cultures, the exposure would often be brief or superficial. In today's business world, international exposure – especially through international travel – is far more common. Such immersive events expose our existing mindsets to alternative ways of thinking. They confront us with different perspectives. No one is immune to those effects. The challenge lies in how we harness these experiences and use these new perspectives.

Any traveler – regardless of whether he or she is underway physically or mentally – can use these immersive events as opportunities to search for new ideas to solve problems. Science fiction thinking, as we will demonstrate throughout this book, shares these immersive qualities with introspection and with international travel, but also adds the futuristic element of time. It is also so eye-opening and transformative that it should also share the same positive perception as other important business tools. By the time you finish this book, we are convinced that you will have found your personal favorite examples of science fiction-to-fact which you can use to activate your own imagination and help others get comfortable with the process.

This comfort level is important. When many people dismissively think of science fiction as a source of entertainment rather than business enlightenment, it might be easy to challenge the idea of whether science fiction thinking has the scope and power to become an important tool for business strategy and innovation. To make the approach work in a business context, some element of escape is necessary. Like a great movie or novel, science fiction thinking endeavors to free us of current limitations so that we can work from the "future back" instead of the "present forward." The more accustomed someone is to the forward but incremental, linear thinking that characterizes many innovation processes, the more that person may initially be uncomfortable with science fiction thinking. One of our main objectives with this book is to make you feel not only more comfortable with this proven process, but also eager to apply it.

Innovation 4.0: Why we are writing this book right now

Mainstream science fiction dates back to the 1800's. Despite science fiction's longevity and its colorful history of inspiring ideas and life-changing products, few people have associated it with serious business strategy and strategic planning. So why do we feel it is important to write a book right now which links science fiction thinking to business strategy and planning?

At first glance, the two may seem to have little in common. That perspective may have been a fair one even just five years ago. But in 2019 and beyond, that perspective is becoming increasingly narrow and limiting. We would argue, in fact, that "science fiction thinking" is now an indispensable tool for enterprises to re-imagine their roles, their purposes, and their financial and commercial opportunities in a time of groundbreaking technological and social changes which are redefining the nature of business in the 21st century. The gap between the genesis of an idea and the technology to realize that idea is shrinking every day. Leaders can already picture their intelligent enterprise empowered with machine learning, blockchain technology, artificial intelligence, augmented and virtual reality, robotics, drones, the internet of things (IoT), and cloud technology. These are just some of the tools which accelerate the transition from the world of science fiction to the tangible products and services that will make a positive difference not only for your customers but also for all your stakeholders and for society at large.

The possibilities from these technologies are so immediate and the potential so overwhelming that they require a conscious measure of discipline and control. This is the fundamental difference between Innovation 4.0 and previous iterations. It makes a break with the narrower "problem-solution" paradigm that has traditionally defined innovation and replaces it with a more overarching "problem-solution-impact" paradigm. In short, we cannot continue to come up with innovative and elegant solutions to problems without also thoroughly understanding the impact those solutions will have, both positive and negative. In the spirit of rapid technological innovation, we already see the first glimpses of Innovation 4.0 on the horizon.

We can express this aspiration in a simple equation which serves as shorthand for this new paradigm:

Innovation 4.0 = [UN Global Goals for Sustainable Development] + [exponential technology] + [Science Fiction Thinking]

Figure 2: Innovation 4.0

This equation underpins the processes described in this book. We will refer to it from time to time as "big problems – big solutions – big impacts". Let's now take a closer look at each variable in the Innovation 4.0 equation.

The source we use to define the "big problems" are the 17 UN Global Goals for Sustainable Development. These goals, shown in Figure 3, describe in succinct and clear terms the most pressing problems the world faces, in a way that will mobilize citizens and encourage enterprises to find ways to solve them. They provide the higher purpose for innovation beyond mere financial and commercial concerns. As we described in the book *SAP Next-Gen: Innovation with Purpose*, the pursuit of a higher purpose and the pursuit of a commercial opportunity are not mutually exclusive. In fact, it is just the opposite. We see a causal link between pursuing a grander purpose and achieving financial and commercial success. The Boston Consulting Group came to a similar conclusion, when it wrote that "holding all other factors equal, companies that outperform in important social and environmental areas achieve higher valuations and higher margins."[7]

Figure 3: The United Nations Global Goals for Sustainable Development

The Global Goals are the inspiration for the "big problems" in our Innovation 4.0 equation because they draw attention to specific areas where an enterprise can focus its attention. The 17 Global Goals define the problems and make them visible. Enterprises around the world are approaching the solutions to these problems from a multitude of perspectives, all the while cognizant that their solutions may create additional problems for them to resolve or mitigate along the way.

But where will the solutions come from, once we can define the problems? Later in Part 1, you will see separate sections in which we imagine the futures of food, work, water, cities, and health care, all from the perspective of science fiction thinking and the available exponential technologies. These technologies, as we noted above, include machine learning, blockchain, artificial intelligence, augmented and virtual reality, robotics, drones, the internet of things (IoT), and cloud technology. The disruptive powers of today's exponential technologies can be daunting in the same way the technologies of the Industrial Revolution in the 1800's met with a mix of visionary optimism and entrenched resistance. This is what makes an understanding of consequences and impacts essential to the 21st century process of innovation. To take the "scary" out of the solutions, an enterprise needs to understand the risks associated with any solution and then consciously mitigate or eliminate them.

Thus, the difference-maker between Innovation 3.0 and Innovation 4.0 is science fiction thinking, a comprehensive approaching to not only changing mindsets and perspectives, but also a means to foresee the impacts – positive and negative – and strike a balance which is beneficial for all stakeholders.

In today's business world we work under the assumption that technology now enables us to achieve any outcome we imagine, if not now, then in a future we can trace a path to. That is a superpower that technology confers on enterprises and the people who manage, shape, and drive them. How can the enterprise employ that superpower as a profitable force for good? That is the key role that science fiction thinking plays, as a way to define and appreciate the outcomes which technology can create. The unforeseen and unexpected negative consequences of a new technology can be as great as the desired and planned-for positive ones. Science fiction thinking, as we will show in this book, helps to temper those extremes to achieve the best possible outcome.

In this manner, science fiction thinking builds the bridge between the United Nations 17 Global Goals for Sustainable Development and the solutions which will ultimately achieve them. As we said in the book *SAP Next-Gen: Innovation with Purpose*, we feel that "linking innovation to purpose and the 17 UN Global Goals can accelerate positive change in the world and improve a company's bottom line." Those efforts can inspire employees, customers, partners, and entire communities to unite around a higher purpose.

How do we launch a collective effort to lead us from the simple but powerful expression of these goals to a world in which we have eradicated the problems which underlie them? How long will it take and what resources will the world need to harness? Innovation 4.0, which introduces science fiction thinking to the "innovation equation," offers a path from today's world to the achievement of these goals.

We feel that these goals' complexity and scope, as well as the amount of time and resources needed to solve them, offer the ultimate challenge to our imagination. Science fiction thinking gives us a means to envision a solution, then formulate and answer the questions we need along the way. It gives intelligent enterprises the ability to work from the "future back" instead of trying to project today into a faraway tomorrow.

In a statement in July 2018, United Nations Secretary-General António Guterres said, "The scale, spread and speed of change made possible by digital technologies is unprecedented, but the current means and levels of international cooperation are unequal to the challenge".

"Digital technologies make a significant contribution to the realization of the Sustainable Development Goals and they cut uniquely across international boundaries," he added. "Therefore, cooperation across domains and across borders is critical to realizing the full social and economic potential of digital technologies as well as mitigating the risks that they pose and curtailing any unintended consequences." [8]

Perhaps the most important role of using science fiction as a guide is therefore its ability to reveal the consequences and impacts of new technologies, far beyond their direct applications. We now assume that previous technological limitations are effectively gone, erased by the convergence between imagination, ideas, and reality. But as technology exploded and created opportunities for exponential growth, our social constructs –regulations, laws, definitions of the common good – have not always kept pace.

Enterprises need a technique, a mindset, and an approach to innovation which keeps pace with the accelerating advancement of technology and at the same time allows the management and the development teams to absorb and envision the impact of the solutions they plan to unleash on the world. It is not a wide-eyed diversion for your team or solely a way to indulge your "inner geek" while at work. By combining technology, vision, and a conscious understanding of the impacts, science fiction thinking offers enterprises a new source of competitive advantage in the 21st century.

As we have said above, science fiction does indeed have a long history of inspiring products and services which have changed the world. In that regard, science fiction thinking is nothing new. In the past, the evolution of science fiction into fact generally happened more in an *ad hoc* fashion. It took place mostly at the fringes, driven by mavericks or by visionaries who had to tell a very convincing story to get the resources they needed to pursue their projects.

Witness the story of Godfrey Hounsfeld, an engineer at EMI's research laboratories in the United Kingdom in the early 1970's. He grappled with a question which pushed the limits of pattern recognition thinking and technology at the time: how can you identify an object within a box without opening the box? As Arthur D. Little consultants P. Ranganath Nayak and John Ketteringham described in their book *Breakthroughs!*, the answer also had links to the technology of the *Star Trek* television series: "The idea was pure science fiction. Hounsfeld was proposing a real-life application of the phenomenon called 'beaming' in the popular television series *Star Trek*." [9] But instead of beaming molecules, Hounsfeld proposed to take a picture of the molecules, "'transport' those pictures on an X-ray into a computer memory, then have the computer reassemble all the little pictures on a monitor screen in exactly their original order." [10]

We know Hounsfeld's device today as the CAT scan.

Fast forward to 2019, and we have the widespread availability of transformative, exponential technologies. For the first time ever, enterprises can conceive, implement, and prosper from a structured process built around science fiction thinking. This approach can become embedded into the enterprise to such an extent that we expect using science fiction thinking as a driver for innovation will become commonplace. The bold ideas resulting from science fiction thinking can now emerge from within the company and its own teams rather than solely being inspired by the creativity of others outside the organization, as in decades past. Thanks to the incredible advances in technology, the time has come for science fiction thinking to come in from the fringes and become a central part of strategic planning and innovation.

That won't happen on its own of course. Enterprises will need engaged managers who are convinced of the power of science fiction thinking, who have activated their own science fiction mindsets, and who will start creating an environment in which others can activate themselves and apply science fiction thinking. It will also require tools and a process, so that the big ideas derived from the world of science fiction do not become products by happenstance or by the energy and drive of a dedicated few inventors such as Martin Cooper and Godfrey Hounsfeld, but rather through the coordinated and sanctioned efforts of the entire organization.

In the spirit of Innovation 4.0, our well-defined approach to turn science fiction thinking from *ad hoc* to commonplace is expressed as the SAP Next-Gen science fiction to fact universe.

Welcome to the SAP Next-Gen science fiction to fact universe

Technology's rapid advancement over the last few years is fusing the real world of businesses together with the imaginary and cautionary worlds which were once the primary domain of science fiction writers and filmmakers. Such a collision, like any one between powerful forces, will have far-reaching effects we are only beginning to observe and understand.

We feel that the upside is immeasurably high.
The challenge is to tap into it.

But where will that creativity come from? What approaches and processes can today's managers use to nurture it and capitalize on it? We feel that the combination of today's businesses with the ideas and impulses of science fiction thinking will unleash business creativity and open vast untapped market potential for those business leaders who recognize and seize the opportunity. The SAP Next-Gen science fiction to fact universe, shown in Figure 4, is the starting point for activating your science fiction inner self, encouraging others to activate theirs, and then defining a process of science fiction thinking in your organization.

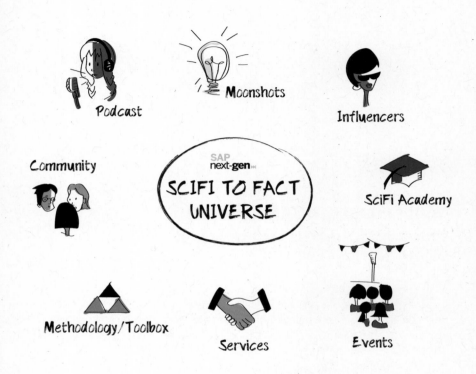

Figure 4: The SAP Next-Gen science fiction to fact universe

The universe encapsulates the five objectives we have
with this book regarding science fiction thinking:

- **Reveal its compelling power and proven history of driving innovation:**
  For years, innovative enterprises have taken once far-fetched ideas found
  in literature or movies (or even cartoons and comic books!) and turned
  them into products and services which have vastly improved people's
  lives around the world. The proven track record of science fiction-to-
  fact is lengthy and undeniable. Chapters 1, 2, and 3 will explore this track
  record and its sources of power in detail.

- **Show you the vast opportunities to apply it:**
  Despite all our technological advances, even in the last few years, the world still faces some seemingly intractable problems. The United Nations has channeled those problems into a set of goals for sustainable development (see Figure 3). SAP is committed to helping enterprises around the world create the ideas, technologies, and products and services which will meet those challenges. In Chapter 4 we will show you how people have started to imagine the future of food, the future of jobs, the future of water, the future of cities, and the future of health care.

- **Activate your science fiction mindset to pursue those opportunities:**
  Anyone can adopt a science fiction mindset. It does not require advance reading or a familiarity with science fiction as much as it requires critical thinking and a commitment to innovation with purpose. It also requires an openness and boldness to think beyond conventional boundaries (time, current technology, current business definitions) and understand the impact of a solution. We see science fiction thinking as a real source of competitive advantage for the intelligent enterprise. Chapter 5 will offer you more encouragement to activate your own science fiction mindset.

- **Set your own stage for Innovation 4.0:**
  Our universe (Figure 4) has many entry points which allow you to gain the knowledge, insights, tools, and techniques to start establishing a process of your own. The feedback we have received is consistently positive, with one management participant claiming that the workshop "helped him learn how to dream again" about the future of his business. We devote Part 2 of this book to the elements of the SAP Next-Gen science fiction to fact universe.

- **Show you how SAP is already supporting enterprises:**
  The tools we introduced in the book *SAP Next-Gen: Innovation with Purpose* continue to evolve and serve as the platforms and the backbone of solutions derived from science fiction thinking. Chapter 8 in Part 2 of the book will show you several examples of how enterprises turned bold ideas into successful products and services.

This book is your passport for the kind of time travel which ignites your imagination and empowers you to bring back ideas which may someday contribute to solving the world's most pressing challenges, as expressed in the Global Goals. SAP Next-Gen uses the "time traveler" analogy to inspire purpose-driven science fiction innovators to picture themselves in the year 2030 and imagine that the UN Global Goals have been achieved. The "time travelers" reflect on the critical actions and commitments that individuals in corporations, governments, academia, institutions, and non-profits made in the intervening years to accelerate the application of digital technologies together to achieve the goals. This time traveler analogy helps people focus on the possibilities and opportunities for achieving positive outcomes rather than being limited by current perceptions of what is possible today.

But to do that, you need to activate your own science fiction thinking. While technical skills, or a familiarity with the science fiction movies or literature, can be advantageous, they are not an absolute prerequisite. Your only basic qualifications to don the science fiction thinking cap are the ability to define a big problem, the intense desire to solve it, and the empathy and willingness to grapple with its impact. The challenge is to activate that mindset within ourselves. This book will offer tools to make that happen and put that mindset to use. Your time immersed in science fiction thinking allows you to take a rich journey through a far-fetched or seemingly impossible future, and then return to the present with the memory of something that made a positive impact for an important reason.

Science fiction thinking doesn't require that you sit down and do exhaustive homework on all the famous authors, or spend weekends binge-watching all the classic movies and television shows. Science fiction itself is a way of thinking, not an entertainment or literary genre.

Part 1 of this book is called "How science fiction thinking fuels Innovation 4.0." It will highlight numerous examples of how many of the products and services we take for granted today – things which continue to make our lives considerably better – trace their origins directly back to ideas which first appeared in science fiction film or literature. These examples of science fiction-to-fact will range from the spectacular to the mundane to the occasionally humorous.

They come from film, from television series, from novels, and even from comic books and other forms of entertainment. What they all have in common, though, is that the inventor or the innovation "borrowed" an idea from a faraway future and put it into the hands of customers, ranging from mainstream consumers to government organizations to institutions aiming to make a difference in people's lives.

"Science fiction readers have access to the future, to a range of futures, actually, and to advanced technology. And we can seriously profit from that capability," award-winning science fiction writer Jack McDevitt said.[11] In McDevitt's statement we would replace "readers" with "thinkers". So, it doesn't necessarily take a heavy-duty set of stories on technology to spur science fiction thinking. He reminds us of this when he suggests a small number of stories that inspired him.

Part 1 will also elaborate on the opportunities where Innovation 4.0 will see its most rigorous application. US President John F. Kennedy once described these challenges as "the unknown, the unanswered, and the unfinished", and we feel that those phrases are apt descriptions of how the world will address the Global Goals in Figure 3. Right now, we do not know all the ways that we can eradicate hunger (Goal #2), vastly expand education opportunities and gender equality (Goals #4 and #5) or take actions to curb or respond to climate change (Goal #13). For the rest of our lifetimes, these goals may still be unfinished business, regardless of how much progress we make. As we will discuss later, numerous attempts to achieve zero hunger have succeeded beyond imagination, but at the same time have left new challenges in their wake. In other words, progress is never perfect. This conflicted nature of progress is what science fiction thinking addresses directly. Nothing we do that is a bold solution to a problem will be perfect or without some risks or negative consequences to mitigate. We will never reach utopia, but we must also understand the potential for negative outcomes, then mitigate or avoid them.

Finally, the logic, facts, background information, and examples in Part 1 will culminate in a chapter about activating your science fiction mindset: what that means, and how you can inspire others to embrace the approach and bring their imaginations to work with them.

Anyone can adopt and embrace science fiction thinking. What makes science fiction thinking special in this regard, though, is its impressive track record of turning imaginative ideas into reality while at the same time revealing, exploring, and understanding the potential downsides. Science fiction thinking is a means to innovate for a better future. The essence of science fiction thinking is combining "what" and a "why" into a compelling vision for the future, without necessarily needing to know precisely right now "how" to make the combination a reality.

In short, the chapters in Part 1 of your journey in this book represent our effort to convince you that science fiction-to-fact is both real, within the capabilities of your business, and a source of considerable competitive advantage as you harness breakthrough technological platforms and innovate with purpose. We want to inspire you to apply it. As you read the examples and the arguments in this book, we hope you will realize quickly that science fiction thinking has been the missing ingredient in your innovation arsenal. It drives creative thinking, changes perspectives, breaks boundaries, and encourages bolder thinking. What seem at first glance like extraordinary or escapist journeys into strange worlds are actually immersive looks into a crystal ball which portend the impact of groundbreaking technological change, both good and bad.

The fact that few businesses have adopted it before, or that it worked its powers in an ad hoc way, is by no means an oversight by business leaders. Until recently, the path from science fiction-to-fact was either too hard to find or too arduous to follow. This was due to technological limitations. Solutions built around machine learning, artificial intelligence, and augmented reality, to name a few, are beginning to erase these limitations. Building on these advancements, how can you and your company envision and participate in a future in which the 17 UN Global Goals are much closer to realization?

Part 2 will introduce you to all the individual parts of the SAP Next-Gen science fiction to fact universe (see Figure 4), which offers business leaders, students, startups and others many ways to find the inspiration, approaches, and tools they need to apply science fiction thinking to their own problems.

Methodology/Toolbox:
Innovation 4.0 and science fiction thinking are actual operational frameworks designed to turn science fiction to fact from an accidental or ad hoc process into something which is commonplace within the 21st century enterprise. A key part of methodology/toolbox is linking innovation projects to one or more of the UN Global Goals, which you can learn about at globalgoals.org/business.

SAP Next-Gen science fiction academy:
This offers students the opportunity to activate their science fiction mindset and use it to apply the latest technologies and methodologies to specific problems.

Community:
In the 21st century world, crowdsourcing has become a common and efficient way to pull ideas, support, and resources together from literally any connected place in the world. Some of the technologies which will enable people to solve the world's most pressing problems are already breaking down barriers of time and distance, allowing not only instant but also continuous communication and contact.

Events:
From our Sci-Fi Wednesday at Hudson Yards in New York City to larger festivals, panels, and conferences around the world, we are constantly facilitating or supporting events which allow community members to engage with each other directly and accelerate their thinking.

Influencers:
Science fiction is nothing new, nor is science fiction to fact. Many entrepreneurs from Richard Branson (Virgin) to Astro Teller (X) to the late novelist Octavia Butler, have served as thought leaders and evangelists for science fiction thinking because they have experienced first-hand how science fiction can inspire people to turn imagination into reality.

Services:
During SAP Next-Gen Boot Camps on science fiction, we spend a day with cross-functional teams to help them activate their science fiction thinking and then apply it to a problem that their enterprise could help solve. By transporting participants anywhere from 10 to 50 years into the future, we start to imagine solutions to these problems and go through the process of working "from the future back". Teams can finish the day with an initial business plan or even a prototype of a solution, but no matter what, they finish the day inspired to continue the search for big solutions to big problems.

Moonshots:
How far do you want to let your imagination go? Moonshot ideas bend the boundaries of our imaginations without breaking them. Throughout history, the boldest visions have often been the ones which gave teams the intense focus and enduring energy to make the seemingly impossible come true.

Podcasts:
Our podcasts help you stay up-to-date on the many facets of science fiction thinking, including the latest ideas and success stories.

Part 2 will conclude with some examples that will demonstrate that our ideas about science fiction thinking are not fiction. Teams from companies and universities across a wide range of backgrounds and industries have started to navigate the SAP Next-Gen science fiction to fact universe successfully and take away insights and ideas which have changed their perspectives, redirected their resources, and invigorated their sense of purpose. They have solved problems in bold, creative ways.

With science fiction thinking and the science fiction to fact universe, SAP Next-Gen is helping not only enterprises but also institutions, governments, and other organizations apply technologies which would have been in the realm of science fiction even just a few years ago. We are empowering companies to bring social purpose to the innovation process through Innovation 4.0, which makes science fiction thinking a fundamental part of disruptive innovation. By breaking with the old "problem-solution" paradigm, the benefits of science fiction thinking – and thus the benefits of Innovation 4.0 – are measurable in financial, commercial, cultural, social, and political terms.

But first you need to start your journey.

PART 1

How science fiction thinking fuels Innovation 4.0

"It's a renaissance, it is a golden age. We are now solving problems with machine learning and artificial intelligence that were ... in the realm of science fiction for the last several decades."

– Jeff Bezos [12]

Understanding the full impact of science fiction

In the context of science fiction thinking, the best formula for innovating with purpose, i.e. to creating big impacts with big solutions to big problems, is [UN Global Goals for Sustainable Development] + [exponential technology] + [Science Fiction Thinking]. This is the essence of Innovation 4.0. By big impacts, we mean the cultural, social, and political impact of the changes, not just the prediction or forecast of the change itself. We mean gaining a critical understanding of who wins and who loses when a disruptive change takes place, even when the change has a huge net benefit for mankind. This is a vital perspective, because it prevents the ideas generated by science fiction from decaying into a purely dystopian outcome. We are not denying that some of the solutions proposed under science fiction thinking – if left unchecked or unmitigated – could give rise to the dystopian visions which underpin many books and movies. Our goal is to raise awareness around the full impact of these bold solutions –positive and negative – rather than entering into science fiction thinking with the naive belief that we can engineer a 100% positive outcome.

Science fiction thinking provides a means to imagine and talk about the impacts. That is a hallmark of the works of science fiction themselves since the first mainstream authors emerged in the 1800's. Their visions were just as liable to draw detractors as to draw in advocates. One fascinating thing about science fiction is that it is normally expressed in the past tense, as if these events decades or centuries away have already happened. It is a "remembered future", as Gerrit Roessler, the program manager at the German Center for Research and Innovation points out.[13] People normally don't play the "what happens if?" game. They look, say, 50 or 100 years into the future and say "look what happened when ..."

Innovative solutions and their underlying technologies are not the whole story. Accelerating the timeline between idea and reality is not a challenge to be solved solely by engineering, design thinking, and lean production. In the rush to craft a solution and bring it to market, it is easy to overlook or underestimate the unintended consequences. An enterprise which does that will be left with few means to mitigate or offset those consequences and impacts when they arise.

The reason is that technology itself is agnostic. It can be easily put to good uses as well as dangerous ones. The ability to do anything with technology triggers an obligation to show responsibility. Up until a few years ago, even some very plausible ideas were subject to technological limitations and would take years to reach the market. Without context and conscience, some technological decisions can go far off track, with dangerous and far-reaching consequences.

In a world where technology essentially allows a business to create anything it wants – limited only by its own imagination and its ability to excite its customers about a better life – businesses require a conscience, a way to guide innovative of use of technology to positive ends. It requires a way to envision and understand the consequences of applying the technology – intended and unintended – rather than rushing from the drawing board to the marketplace. The impacts of innovations transcend the purely financial and commercial considerations, but they are not divorced from them. Science fiction, in contrast, thrives on these moral, ethical, and societal conflicts and offers us a forum to discuss them with some detachment and think how they apply to our lives today. In the book *SAP Next-Gen: Innovation with Purpose* we argued that pursuing a greater purpose – the conscience and compass for the business – can actually lead to better financial performance and not only a contribution to the greater societal good. These two aspects are neither mutually exclusive, nor merely complementary or correlated. We believe that there is a true cause-and-effect relationship.

Science fiction to fact is accelerating … and changing our lives quickly

Science fiction thinking is uniquely positioned to help anyone imagine the big solutions and the big impacts when they apply technology to a major problem. Our mission with this multi-faceted framework is to make science fiction thinking mainstream when a company engages in its innovation process. The scope of the framework provides business leaders with many ways to imagine big innovative solutions to big problems, while weighing the potential positive and negative impacts at the same time. The universe in Figure 4 is not about technological enablement. It is about innovation with purpose and reaping the greatest benefits from technology by steering its use in the right direction. This, again, is where science fiction thinking comes in, because it not only offers us the means to envision the grand solution, but also appreciate the impact that solution will have – positive and negative – on all stakeholders and society.

Science fiction thinking takes place in those fertile gray areas between faintly plausible and totally crazy, between the pursuit of utopia and the avoidance of dystopia, and between fiction and fantasy. Science fiction thinking is a powerful way to envision purposeful solutions for a sustainable future.

Think back to our story in the introduction about Robert Goddard, one of the fathers of modern rocketry. Forty years later, what we now look back on as the Space Age was well underway, with the "space race" and the Apollo program capturing the world's imagination. A short story by legendary science fiction writer Arthur C. Clarke inspired the 1968 movie *2001: A Space Odyssey*. Stanley Kubrick directed the landmark film and co-wrote the screen play with Clarke. Through the talking computer Hal, Kubrick said he wanted to convey "the reality of a world populated – as ours soon will be – by machine entities that have as much, or more, intelligence as human beings. We wanted to stimulate people to think what it would be like to share a planet with such creatures." [14]

That world has arrived. Alexa, the voice-activated assistant from Amazon, is a distant but direct relative of the computer Hal. Now companies such as Google and Amazon are focusing on how to use contextual data to make the assistants more intuitive in the way a human assistant would be. [15] Where will that lead? One person who feels he knows the answer is American author and futurist Ray Kurzweil. As Figure 5 shows, he feels the time is imminent when machines know more collectively than humans do.

"2029 is the consistent date I have predicted for when an AI will pass a valid turing test and therefore achieve human levels of intelligence. I have set the date 2045 for the 'Singularity' which is when we will multiply our effective intelligence a billion fold by merging with the intelligence we have created."

RAY KURZWEIL
(Futurism.com article October 2017)

Figure 5: When will machines be collectively smarter than we are?

These are two of many examples which show that we live our personal and professional lives in a dreams-come-true world once imagined by science fiction writers, filmmakers, futurists, and the people they inspired with their works. We are startled by many things we experience today in our personal and professional lives which originated in movies, novels, and even cartoons and comic books. But we shouldn't be. The truth is that we are surrounded by so many products and services that originated in movies, books, and television shows that we take now them for granted. Doesn't it seem like you are reading the expression "no longer science fiction" more and more often?

Think about the immense positive changes that technologies – dreamed up years, decades, or even centuries earlier – have brought about. A hundred years ago, the average person never traveled more than 3,000 miles in a lifetime outside of their own town. And now we do that in one plane trip. Two thirds of all human beings in the year 2000 had never made a phone call. In 2019 the number of mobile phone users in the world is expected to pass the five billion mark.[16]

You can't stop this kind of technological progress. You shouldn't stop it. You shouldn't be scared about it. It is just going to happen. And it is especially critical in the era of extreme change and disruption we find ourselves in. So, science fiction to fact has always been a powerful presence in our lives. There is nothing unique about that progression in the past, present, or future. It is normal. What is different and compelling now is that the pace of innovation is rapidly increasing; consequently, the time gap between initial concept and real-world implementation is shrinking. That is more than an assertion or a general impression which "feels" true. We can measure this rapid technological acceleration based on product diffusion, which is the rate at which products go from the drawing board to near complete market penetration. To take just one example, the microwave oven took around 25 years to go from its mainstream commercial launch in 1967 to 80% household penetration in the United States. But before that, it took the Raytheon Corporation over 20 years to evolve the device's main component (the magnetron) from its use in World War II as a radar component. The steps went from its original experimental application for cooking (of course, first tested with popcorn!)[17], to the commercial patent in 1946, to the launch of the household *Radarange* together with the US-based appliance maker Amana in 1967.[18] Likewise, the VCR needed around 25 years to go from launch – primarily to institutions – to achieve 80% household penetration, but less than 25 years after that to disappear into almost complete obsolescence.[19]

Now let's think again of the facts behind the evolutionary path from the *Star Trek* communicator we saw on television screens in the 1960's to the smartphones we use today. It took over five years for Martin Cooper and his team at Motorola to make the very first mobile phone call, another 10 years before the first commercial cellular phones hit the market in 1983, and yet another 10 years again before the phones became mainstream.[20] The Blackberry didn't hit the market until 1999, and the Apple iPhone did not launch until 2007, over 40 years after *Star Trek* debuted.[21] [22]

The 40-year path from the debut of Star Trek (1966) to the debut of the Apple iPhone (2007) – similar to the evolution of the microwave oven and the VCR – is glacial compared to the pace of technological development we witness today. In less than 10 years after its launch, the smartphone achieved market penetration rates of more than 80% in many countries, making it one of the most rapidly dispersed technological products in human history. A recent report by Deloitte describes mobile technology as "a fixture of modern life. So much so, that people without access to mobile devices are severely limited in their ability to participate in the full spectrum of today's economic and societal activities." [23]

What will be the first product or service to break the new benchmark for diffusion established by the smartphone? All we know for certain is that the explosively rapid penetration of the smartphone is a record to be broken, and we have no doubt that it will be broken repeatedly. The only question is what those products will be and which companies – or collaborative group of companies – will lead the charge.

The graphic in the *New York Times* article from 2008, which we just cited, shows visually that product diffusion for technological products has been getting more and more compressed and accelerated since the telephone and the phonograph at the turn of the 19th century. Better said, such rapid diffusion of technological advancements should be commonplace.

One of the most exciting aspects of what we describe in this book is that the underlying ideas for the next breakthroughs to conquer the world likely already exist in the words, images, and spellbinding stories of science fiction. As you will see time and again throughout this book, science fiction worlds are the wellspring of many ideas which have provided big solutions to big problems, with a large net positive impact of mankind. There are many things we haven't seen yet but which are emerging now. In the past, the ingredients to transform science fiction into science fact were inspiration, energy, and time as technology caught up with imagination. With the gap between imagination and technological reality now shrinking, it's time to add some process and structure to that path so that companies can harness those technologies and seize opportunities to solve some of the world's most pressing problems. That is one of the main purposes of this book.

Of course, the path from fiction to fact is not guaranteed. If we asked you to put down your smartphone, look out the nearest window, and tell us how many flying cars you see, you would probably grin and answer "none." There are no flying DeLoreans with Mr. Fusions and flux capacitors. But what would you think if we said you are taking the question too literally? Perhaps you aren't looking closely enough. It is a matter of perspective.

While we may not yet have flying cars as mainstream products to transport our bodies, we do have numerous ways to transport our faculties – our senses and our consciousness – into places we could only dream of traveling to just a few short years ago. This ability is no longer a "superpower" in a comic-book hero sense, but rather a way people around the world are solving problems faster, more efficiently, and more effectively than ever before.

A few years before Stanley Kubrick and Arthur C. Clarke worked together to bring *2001: A Space Odyssey* to the screen, moviegoers were treated to the Academy-Award-winning science fiction film *Fantastic Voyage*, which told a story with the following plot:

> *A scientist is nearly assassinated. To save him, a submarine [called Proteus] is shrunken to microscopic size and injected into his blood stream with a small crew. Problems arise almost as soon as they enter the bloodstream.* [24]

That movie inspired the 1987 movie Innerspace. In today's vernacular we would replace the word "submarine" in the plot of *Fantastic Voyage* with "drone." When innovators can't find a way to transport human beings to another place, they work instead on transporting our senses instead. Can technology now take our senses *inside* the body, not with the resolution of a 19th-century technology such as the X-ray machine or with the 20th century capabilities of a CT scan, but rather with the microscopic precision one might expect from 21st century medicine? What would drones help doctors discover within our bodies?

Here is where science fiction-to-fact is starting to take hold again. The idea of a small exploratory device which transports our senses into environments we otherwise could not reach is now becoming more important in medicine. The company Proteus Digital Health is now placing sensors in the bloodstream or in pills.[25] In 2017, the US Food and Drug Administration approved the first "digital pill" called Abilify MyCite.[26] The pill – which is a treatment for psychosis – contains a sensor which tracks whether a patient has taken the pill as described. This monitoring of medicine usage is important, not only for patient welfare but also from an economic standpoint. IMS estimates that the "improper and unnecessary use of medicine cost the US healthcare sector over $200 billion in 2012." [27]

True to the dynamic of technological upsides and downsides we described above, the existence of Ability MyCite and its approval by the FDA immediately gave rise to worries about unintended consequences and unproven effects. A balanced article published by the American Psychiatric Association, however, concluded with an acknowledgment that efforts had apparently been taken to recognize potential concerns: "Some people may be jumping to negative conclusions because it is easy to confuse this with applications that aren't proven, that don't ensure privacy, and that don't require a physician. This is a case where the FDA, researchers, and ethicists are trying to bring stability in the wild, wild west." [28]

With this book, we are also trying to bring some stability and coherence to what could easily become a "wild West" of innovation, when technology makes anything possible but also demands that we act responsibly and innovate for the greater good. Science fiction thinking has a decisive role to play as an innovation driver in today's intelligent enterprises. But it demands a thorough understanding and a clear approach so that the new benefit of the solutions you develop not only serve a higher purpose, but achieve an enduring net benefit for your enterprise, your customers, and society at large.

Let's explore the SAP Next-Gen science fiction to fact universe further.

The compelling power
of science fiction thinking

"Science fiction, in simplest terms, sets you free," says Ralph Osterhout, chief executive of the Osterhout Design Group, which builds augmented reality glasses.[29] But how does it accomplish that? What is the source of power behind science fiction thinking?

Think back to how author Eliot Peper described it in his *Harvard Business Review* article: "Science fiction isn't useful because it's predictive. It's useful because it reframes our perspective on the world. Like international travel or meditation, it creates space for us to question our assumptions."[30]

As we said in the introduction, one of our main objectives with this book, especially in this second chapter, is to make you feel not only more comfortable with these proven process, but also eager to apply them. But the inverted direction of science fiction thinking (e.g. the "future back" approach) is not the only aspect which will require the achievement of a comfort level. People also need to become comfortable with the boldness of a solution, to let themselves go without any fear of being labeled "crazy" or being accused of imagining very far-reaching impacts, whether positive or negative.

When we start to connect science fiction stories with the Global Goals and technologies that drive innovation, we can find many examples where these are all in alignment in a way that leads to a positive outcome while mitigating the risks of unintended consequences.

We will now exercise your thinking for you to tap into this compelling mindset by going through a number of examples that show how science fiction became science fact and where you see the clear link to Innovation 4.0 represents combining emerging technologies, purpose, and science fiction thinking. By illustrating those examples we are not saying that the inventors of today were inspired by a specific science fiction movie, but rather that when looking back at science movies of the past one can see how today new technologies have emerged that can be recognized in the past films.

In the 1968 film "Fantastic Voyage," five people were shrunk down to fit into a microscopic submarine that could enter a human body and combat diseases at the cellular level. While we don't shrink humans, we now benefit from technology like smart pills that extend our human senses through sensor technology that is small enough to course through the avenues of a human body.[31] Additionally, tiny autonomous vehicles the width of a human hair have been used to treat diseases in the stomachs of mice.[32] Figure 6 illustrates how an emerging technology that we see today can be recognized in a science fiction film of the past, and how today's new technologies are also driving positive impact aligned with the UN Global Goals.

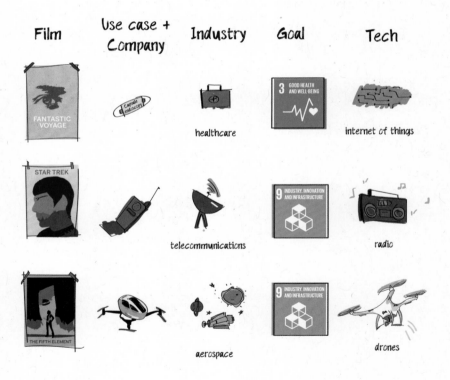

Figure 6: Illustrations of today's new technologies that one can recognize in science fiction movies of the past.

As mentioned at the introduction to this book, Motorola's flip phone designer Martin Cooper was inspired by the handheld mobile communicator devices depicted in the 1960s Star Trek television series. Beyond just the mobile handset, we must also credit the infrastructure of the telecommunications industry which has enabled nearly ubiquitous mobile phone service.
See Figure 6 for an illustration.

The 1997 film "The Fifth Element" featured flying cars & taxis as urban transportation. Today, Chinese drone maker Ehang has produced the Ehang 184 Autonomous Aerial Vehicle capable of transporting a person.[33]
See Figure 6 for an illustration.

Flying cars may soon join that science fiction to fact group after all. In a July 2018 story with the headline "From Impossible to Inevitable", CBS News broke a story about Blackfly, which is essentially a drone large enough to seat a single person. Why haven't we seen these cars already?

With respect to flying cars in the spirit of Blackfly "the technology wasn't there," explains Willie Turner, vice president of operations for the Hiller Aviation Museum in Silicon Valley. "Because they didn't have the computers. And now the computers can actually manipulate the controls." [34]

Turner's answer is in line with what we have said all along. It has historically taken decades for technology to catch up with our imaginations. Now it happens in a small number of years, in some cases an entire order of magnitude faster than it used to. With the advent of machine learning, artificial intelligence, and virtual and augmented reality, it is reasonable to expect that this rapidly declining lag between concept and reality will compress even further, perhaps even to a matter of months.

Blackfly's developers would like to start marketing the vehicle in 2019 for the price of an SUV. Uber is also working on developing a flying taxi. If all of this sounds vaguely familiar, perhaps you are thinking of the movie *The Fifth Element*, where drone-like flying vehicles were central to the plot.

Why has it been so hard to introduce flying cars? The efforts of Blackfly and many others in this exciting field represent both the need and the nature of Innovation 4.0. The idea of flying cars is finally emerging from science fiction, because the technology to do it finally caught up with our ability to imagine that world. But it will take science fiction thinking to help these vehicles enter the mainstream, and then become as commonplace as so many science fiction inspired innovations before them. There are two reasons for this: first, the dramatic impact these technologies may have, and second, the fact that current legal and social systems are not yet ready to accept them.

"Flying autonomous vehicles could make transportation fast, convenient and efficient, but would require huge social, political, and regulatory changes," according to 2017 report from Gartner, cited in an article by ZDNet.[35] That is the essence of "big problems – big solutions – big impacts" and the kinds of challenges which science fiction thinking is ideally suited to address. Nonetheless, it is worth taking a closer look at where the world of flying cars stands now, how far it has progressed, and what lies in store.

Flying cars have been a staple of science fiction, from serious works to the animated 1960's television series *The Jetsons* (which, by the way, also featured robotic household servants and the kinds of video communication we now conduct regularly over our tablets, phones, and PC's!). One problem lies in the name itself. The term "flying car" is what we would refer to as a "past-forward" or "present-forward" phrase. Instead of working from the future back, and "remembering" a future time when we have solved the idea of safe, aerial point-to-point transportation, we have been semantically and scientifically trapped into finding ways to make a two-ton object designed to be completely terrestrial (a "car") and adapting it to operate it enter a foreign environment in an alien way ("flying"). By focusing instead on what it means for a human to move about in a safe way above ground and divorcing ourselves from the current traditional perceptions of a "car", it is much easier to imagine ourselves piggybacking on a larger version of the recreational drone.

Blackfly's initiative with drones starts to unburden the concept – linguistically and practically – from past notions on the flying car. A project announced by the carmaker Audi AG and the Germany city Ingolstadt takes that idea one step further. Referring only to "mobility in the third dimension", the city and Audi announced a joint project with the European Union to test air taxi operations in the Ingolstadt area.[36] The same announcement did not envision a world dominated by such vehicles, but rather saw them as a complement to other surface-based technologies. "Connected, electric and autonomous cars will make urban traffic more comfortable and cleaner and will save space – that means better quality of life for people in cities. This is where mobility in the third dimension can make a valuable contribution in the future."

The vehicles for this pilot project come from a joint venture between Audi, its subsidiary Italdesign, and the aerospace company Airbus. Called Pop.Up.Next and described as a hybrid between a self-driving car and a passenger drone, the prototype was unveiled at the Geneva Autosalon in early 2018. The lightweight, two-passenger vehicle features a 49-inch screen in its cabin. Interaction between humans and the machine takes place through voice and face recognition, eye tracking, and a touch function.[37]

The city of Dubai got a head start on this kind of idea in 2017 when it tested passenger drones from the German aircraft manufacturer Velocopter. The German company has a partnership with Intel, has also made test flights in the United States, and has received an investment of $30 million from Daimler.[38]

In discussing the relationship between Velocopter and Intel, what source of inspiration did Brian Krzanich, then the CEO of Intel, cite to the audience? It was science fiction, of course, the form of *The Jetsons*.

"Fifty-five years ago, the TV show *The Jetsons* first aired and showed us a future where flying cars were a part of everyday life," he said. "We're on the cusp of making that a reality. Imagine pulling out your phone, opening a transportation app and summoning your own personalized ride by air taxi. That sci-fi vision of the future is actually much closer than you may think." [39]

Dubai has also agreed to tests with the Chinese manufacturer Ehang. [40] [41] Ehang claims that between 50 and 100 companies around the world are currently working on this kind of technology. [42] It is undeniable that the market for drones in general, not just passenger drones, is attractive. Goldman Sachs estimates total sales of drones at $100 billion between 2016 and 2020, with $30 billion of that generated by consumer, commercial, and civil demand. [43]

In addition to these examples, we would like to highlight how SAP solutions support customers in a variety of industries from around the world, with the stories all told in terms of "big problems – big solutions – big impacts."

Saving every last drop: Water in India [44]

Water scarcity is creating crisis conditions across much of India. A pioneering manufacturer joined forces with SAP to confront the challenges and develop solutions.

Big problem:
India is facing a water crisis significantly more complex than any in the nation's history. It is a crisis brewed by centuries of water mismanagement, population growth, climate change, pollutants, lack of water storage, inadequate sanitation and waste water treatment, and widespread declining rainfall.

Could Vectus and SAP find ways to help those affected to live better, healthier lives, with clean water and safe, water-conserving products?

Big Solution:
A frustrating obstacle was standing in the way of Vectus' goals: their slow and inadequate legacy IT system. By replacing it with SAP S/4 HANA, the company quickly digitized its core processes and started exploring how mobile and internet of things (IoT) technologies could help them save as much water as possible.

Big Impact:
With better insights, Vectus was able to pinpoint one of the primary water waste culprits: the leaky water pipe.

With increased access to clean water, people can lead healthier lives — with less risk of infection and communicable disease. Environmental conditions can improve. Farmers can increase their crop yields, feeding more people. And perhaps most importantly, countries around the world can save precious water for future generations.

Smarter safety: Earthquakes in Japan [45]

In earthquake-prone Japan, a manufacturing company is working to improve seismic monitoring and protect citizens. Smart phones and SAP technology are keys to greater safety.

Big problem:
Earthquakes – from minor tremors to more serious events – are almost daily occurrences in Japan. Nowhere is the concern more acute than in skyscraper-dominated Tokyo, a city particularly vulnerable to earthquakes. According to experts, there is a 70 percent chance of a magnitude 7-class earthquake in the Tokyo area by 2042. So how can the country protect its citizens?

Seismic monitoring can detect and measure the intensity of shaking, but it can do little to estimate structural integrity of buildings or the risk to the people within them. The Japanese manufacturing company Hakusan thought there must be a better way.

Big Solution:
Hakusan discovered the perfect low-cost seismometer to attach to buildings: the smart phone. They built an app to measure impact, but then they realized that they couldn't process the hundreds of thousands of data points fast enough to understand what the data revealed. They needed a technology partner and chose SAP.

SAP HANA and SAP Cloud Platform provided the solution – with a simple, intuitive user interface; in-memory computing to handle data from as many as 100,000 devices; and analytics to quickly determine the damage from an earthquake event.

Big Impact:
Earthquakes pose a threat to billions of people in almost every part of the world. With a vision for change and the right technology, it is now possible to reduce the associated risks. The Hakusan/SAP solution can be extended anywhere earthquake disaster could strike, potentially saving countless lives.

––––––––

It is now worth taking a closer and deeper look at what science fiction thinking means. To guide and channel our thinking, we needed to reconcile the many views and influences on what science fiction thinking is and establish a crisp definition and a proper context.

Science fiction thinking in literal terms

Imagining a better life is as old as mankind itself. Imagining that better life through modern science has its roots at least as far back as the Renaissance, when Leonardo Da Vinci first conceived of the "what" and "why" for his flying machine, even though he couldn't get the "how" figured out sufficiently to make it fly. If we think literally and simply, we could start with the terms themselves and blend them.

Science is a systematically organized body of knowledge on a particular subject. It is governed by established principles and theories. **Fiction** is a story or setting that is derived from imagination – in other words, not based strictly on history or fact. When we combine the two, we can define science fiction as imagined scenarios based on technological or scientific advancements. It is a future scenario that adheres to a set of scientific knowledge that is not yet established as fact. This describes many of the devices, personalities, and lifestyles we observe in movies and books.

But despite Arthur C. Clarke's Third Law, which states that "[a]ny sufficiently advanced technology is indistinguishable from magic," we must recognize and enforce a boundary between fiction and fantasy.[46] As we explain in more detail in Chapter 3, the world of science fiction is not the realm of unicorns and magic spells.

Though depending on the era someone grew up in, some confusion around fiction and fantasy is understandable. In 1950 Alan Turing codified what became known as the Turing Test, a way to determine whether a robot or android is indistinguishable from a human.[47] When it becomes commonplace for these machines to be indistinguishable from human beings, it gives rise to a range of critical questions: how do we treat them? Are they life forms that we need to respect? These questions are relevant today.

In the 1999 film Bicentennial Man, a robot named "Andrew" interacts autonomously with his human associates. That movie was based on Isaac Asimov's 1976 novelette of the same name, which he published as part of his *Robot* series. Today we see "Sophia," a humanoid robot from Hansen robotics based in Hong Kong,[48] not only interacting as an artificial intelligence with United Nations leaders like UN Deputy Secretary-General Amina Mohammed, but also becoming designated as a Saudi Arabian citizen.

In October 2017 the United Nations held a conference called "The Future of Everything – Sustainable Development in the Age of Rapid Technological Change."[49] When asked about the lack of internet services and electricity in some parts of the world, the humanoid robot, Sophia, quoted science fiction author William Gibson by saying "the future is already here.

It's just not very evenly distributed." But she added that "If we are smarter and focused on win-win type of results, A.I. [artificial intelligence] could help proficiently distribute the world's existing resources like food and energy." [50]

That same panel raised questions which reinforced the scope we have defined under Innovation 4.0, as described in our equation shown in Figure 2 as well as our mantra of "big problems – big solutions – big impacts". Marie Chatardová, president of the UN Economic and Social Council (ECOSOC), said "[w]e are only starting to see the benefits, but we do need to assess the risks of these technologies." [51]

One month after that conference, the United Nations Development Program (UNDP) in Asia-Pacific appointed Sophia its Innovation Champion, making her the first non-human to receive any kind of honor from the UN. One of Sophia's objectives, aligned with the spirit of this book, is to support the 17 UN Global Goals for Sustainable Development (see Figure 3). [52]

Sophia's origins and the background of her creator, David Hanson, point once again to the compelling power of science fiction. The lifelike Sophia relies on voice-recognition and face-recognition technologies combined with artificial intelligence. If her appearance is reminiscent of the animatronic figures one sees at amusement parks such as Walt Disney World, that should come as no surprise. Hanson worked for the company as an "imagineer," specifically as a sculptor and technical consultant. [53] Disney, as we will mention in Chapter 4, spent years envisioning the Experimental Prototype Community of Tomorrow (EPCOT), which would have been an actual city to test new technologies and community forms rather than the theme park it eventually became.

The **thinking** part has several important dimensions, however. We could have stopped short and called this new approach "science fiction design" or something similar. But that is too narrow and too focused on the technology, rather than the broader implications and impacts. Amidst the rapid technological changes right now, it is not only unwise or irresponsible to uncouple technology from its impact in the innovation process. It is virtually impossible to do so.

Because technology is agnostic, it is up to us to infuse its use consciously and proactively with purpose and guide the course of its impact to the greatest degree possible.

One is the mechanical aspect of applying science fiction to contemporary business or societal problems. What problems can we solve if we had certain technological or scientific advancements at our disposal? But thinking also has the aspect of thoughtfulness, mindfulness, and critical thinking in our context as well. What are the impacts of solving that problem? Do the scientific advances which solve one problem create others? And what do mean by the word "problem" anyway?

Given the unprecedented rate of technological change now, science fiction thinking is more relevant than ever. But it is not a completely new concept. These comments from the World Economic Forum echo the definition and context we have provided for science fiction thinking so far.

- **Inspiration and Power:**
  "Researchers and designers of interactive technologies have been inspired by science fiction to create novel devices, products and systems that change traditional ways of doing things or using technology." [54]

- **Recognizing the impacts:**
  "The best sci-fi stories mix two ingredients. The first is great science which sometimes leads to surprising accuracy. The second ingredient is a keen understanding of contemporary hopes and fears." [55]

- **Bold fiction to breakthrough fact:**
  The defining feature of our days is that we feel like we live in an era of incredible innovation, mostly thanks to staggering breakthroughs in science and technology." [56]

Breaking down science fiction thinking in that literal manner allows us to build a bridge to the innovation processes at a company. Iterative innovation is usually driven by "problem-solution" way of thinking. That is why the term "design thinking" has become so widely adopted. Science fiction thinking provides two supplemental elements: the **scale of the problem** and the **impacts of the solution**. This enhances the flow of big problem - big solution - big impacts

How do we envision the scale?

This is indeed a challenge. But it is also one reason why we framed up the SAP Next-Gen science fiction to fact universe (see Figure 4) as a wheel with multiple entry points rather than a chain of thought or a process with a fixed starting point and predefined cumulative steps. Whatever aspect of the universe appeals to you, start there, pursue it, and use it. The additional perspectives and insights should help you see along a longer and bolder timeline to the future you imagine, so that you can "remember" that future and start to work backwards from it to today. In this manner, we help you break away from the endemic "past-forward" and "present-forward" thinking which suppresses or constrains innovation potential, and instead work with a future back mentality.

One risk with this flow, however, is imagining both the problem and the impacts too narrowly. Probable root causes of that skepticism are the inability to imagine a much different (and better life) and a reluctance to look far beyond the current time horizons, then to work backwards from that future. If all you have ever consumed at breakfast is black coffee, it is hard to imagine an espresso or a cappuccino. Even some of the smartest minds can fall victim to this trap of narrow thinking which draws predominantly on a projected past rather than a remembered future.

Do you recall when we said that the smartphone has perhaps the most rapid penetration of any technology in the history of mankind? About 40 years ago, AT&T asked a leading consulting firm for an estimate of the total market for the nascent technology we now know as the ubiquitous cellphone. As noted by *The Economist*, the consultants cited the "absurdly heavy" weight of the devices, the poor battery life and coverage, and the high price, and arrived at its answer: a total market of 900,000 users! [57] Apparently, the vision of the Star Trek communicator – the very device which inspired Motorola's Martin Cooper to develop the device in the first place – had not inspired or influenced the consultants sufficiently.

Eliot Peper referred to this kind of narrow thinking and inability to see beyond the time horizon as the "manure dystopia". He cites the fact that in the late 1800's the streets of Manhattan were covered with 45,000 tons of manure every month thanks to horse-driven transportation. Peper notes that "[i]f 19th-century urban planners had had access to big data, machine learning techniques, and modern management theory, these tools would not have helped them. They simply would have confirmed their existing concerns. Extrapolating from past trends is useful but limiting in a world of accelerating technological change." [58]

The solution in Manhattan, of course, was to imagine a city without the horses. Fast forward over 100 years, and the world confronts another dramatic set of transportation problems. There are now over 1 billion automobiles on the world's roads, and the chief economist of British Petroleum (BP) forecasts that that number will grow to 2 billion by 2040, with 320 million of them powered by electricity. [59]

One of the biggest technological challenges for electricity-powered vehicles is to make batteries more powerful and less expensive at the same time. An 2015 article in the *MIT Technology Review* described the difficulties in achieving that dynamic, but did note that by working together with Panasonic since 2008, the car company Tesla had achieved some success in that area. "Since 2008, the cost of Tesla's battery packs has been cut approximately in half, while storage capacity has increased by about 60 percent," the article said. [60] The quest to continue this kind of dynamic improvement has taken on the character of an "arms race" between Tesla, Chinese companies, and German companies. [61] The truth is that we have always imagined the future of cities. In Chapter 4 we will show an example of people imagining what the city of Chicago might look like in the year 2068, if flooding starts to threaten both cities and fresh water suppliers along the heavily populated coasts of the United States.[62] But if we want to take the idea of imagining a city one step further, we can move far beyond the competitions sponsored by Audi. We can move beyond the futuristic cities envisioned by Walt Disney with his Experimental Prototype Community of Tomorrow (EPCOT), in which "Walt expected things that people have been hoping for, twenty-five and thirty years in the future" and which he predicted would be the "first accident-free, noise free, pollution free city center in America." [63] That place we can move onto is called Neom, a $500-billion megacity planned for the Saudi Arabian desert. We will take a closer look at Neom in Chapter 4 as well.[64]

Science fiction thinking, as we elaborate in this book, is the antidote to that problem of limited perspectives and narrow visions. Instead of trying to project today's soon-to-be-obsolete reality into the future, science fiction thinking works from the future backwards. Science fiction offers us fully-formed worlds which show the *impacts* of the technology, which can be cultural, social, and political. The movies and novels which are the rich and proven source material for our better future are populated with more than the gadgets and lifestyles we hope for. They show us worlds where technology transforms society.

The roots and psychology of science fiction thinking

Science fiction thinking is not a buzzword phrase or a gimmick. It has its roots in how we read and interpret stories, how we immerse in them, and how they affect us. One key aspect of this is the detachment we referred to earlier. Technically speaking this is known as estrangement. The idea of estrangement – the ability to separate ourselves from reality while remaining tethered to it – is one source of the power of science fiction.

But estrangement is also a matter of context and degree. We need to distinguish between the desirable and the mystical. One popular question today is "if you were a superhero, what superpower would you choose?" Many of these superpowers people cite lie squarely in the realm of fantasy. They are the names of spells in games such as Dungeons & Dragons (invisibility, teleportation, flying, water breathing) or the effects we expect from the wizards in the Harry Potter canon. This is where we need to draw an important line between fiction and fantasy. Sticking with the *Harry Potter* analogy, we need to push the boundaries of the "muggle" world as close to the wizard world as possible, but we cannot cross the line. What that means in our context is that science fiction thinking requires us to suspend reality, but still have a hint of plausibility, no matter how tenuous. The tether to our current world is not cut completely. We don't have carte blanche to make things up. There must always be a definable path and a process to the new world we are envisioning under "Life will be better when …", even if that "how" is, to use John F. Kennedy's phrase, currently unknown, unanswered, or unfinished.

If we cut that tether, no matter how tenable it is, we veer off into the world of fantasy with dragons, unicorns, and magic. But when we push the limits the right way, this estrangement or detachment means we can pull ourselves away from the present and think about problems, solutions, and impacts without our own "present" being a drag on the process.

Literary critic Darko Suvin uses the term cognitive estrangement to describe a situation where someone immersed in science fiction manages the degree to which he or she suspends disbelief. It builds on a definition of estrangement put forward by Bertolt Brecht: "A representation which estranges is one which allows us to recognize its subject, but at the same time makes it seem unfamiliar." [65]

There is growing mainstream recognition that some of the most successful people in the world right now have been inspired by science fiction. More importantly, though, is the fact that people are beginning to understand that science fiction thinking is actually a viable framework for accelerating innovation. That idea has long been implicit, but we are now able to isolate and motivate how science fiction thinking works and apply it more broadly to the biggest challenges we face in the early 21st century and beyond. Far from being the exclusive realm of geeks and geniuses, science fiction thinking is accessible and on its way to becoming a standard way of thinking about and achieving innovation with purpose and with a clear understanding of the cultural and societal impacts.

"Science fiction may seem trivial to blind critics and philosophers of today," the writer Isaac Asimov once said. "But the core of science fiction has become crucial to our salvation if we are to be saved at all. I do not fear computers, I fear the lack of them." [66]

One inherent ability of science fiction, as we have mentioned before, is its ability to help us envision and think through the consequences of technology and the far-reaching impact it can have on how we live our lives. Science fiction has given the world transformative technologies and shown us ways that people – albeit fictional ones – have dealt with the disruptions and transitions which these new technologies caused. When we enter their worlds, they become our avatars, our conversation partners, our inspiration to grasp how to remember that future and work back to today.

The pioneering science fiction writer Octavia Butler was aware of this point and reminded readers of it in a piece she published in Essence magazine in 2000. Her comment is a reminder for keeping "big impacts", the final part of the Innovation 4.0 mantra, ever-present in our thinking.

"I realized that I didn't believe there were any medications that had no side effects." she wrote. "In fact, I don't believe we can do anything at all without side effects–also known as unintended consequences. Those consequences may be beneficial or harmful. They may be too slight to matter, or they may be worth the risk because the potential benefits are great, but the consequences are always there." [67] The other part of that mantra is "big problem – big solutions". Would you believe that it may be easier to solve big problems than small ones? Astro Teller of X (formerly Google X) feels that way and has a logical defense for that belief which ties back to Innovation 4.0, science fiction thinking, and exponential growth. In a TED talk, as reported in *Wired* [68], Teller said that "It's often easier to make something 10 times better than it is to make it 10 percent better. Because when you're working to make things 10 percent better, you inevitably focus on the existing tools and assumptions, and on building on top of an existing solution that many people have already spent a lot of time thinking about. But when you aim for a 10x gain, you lean instead on bravery and creativity – the kind that, literally and metaphorically, can put a man on the moon." In other words, big solutions come when you work from the future back, not from the past or present forward.

Science fiction thinking is also a gift from one generation to the next, a pattern we hope to encourage and support with this book. It is vital for science fiction to keep telling its story once the fiction becomes fact, to inspire another generation which can help other ideas follow that same science fiction to fact path. Gwynne Shotwell, the president and COO of SpaceX, said she became an engineer after an inspiring meeting with a female mechanical engineer when she was a teenager. "I think it's important to be as public as I can afford to be and to hopefully inspire women to join me in this incredible field," Shotwell told CNBC in an interview. Shotwell said she also wants the activities of SpaceX to get "young children thinking about being in the space industry again." [69]

We never know when an idea or spark we experienced in childhood can trigger fresh ideas when we become adults. Most of us know what a taser is but did not know that the word is an acronym like laser ("Light Amplification by Stimulated Emission of Radiation") and scuba (Self-Contained Underwater Breathing Apparatus). When NASA physicist Jack Cover invented the taser, he drew inspiration from a character named Tom Swift, a genius protagonist in pulp children's fiction. Swift lent his name to the new device: "Thomas A. Swift's Electric Rifle." [70]

In the next chapter we explore the immense underlying power of science fiction thinking and show how it applies to the world's biggest challenges (as expressed in the 17 UN Global Goals). We will show the ways that these inventions – many inspired directly by science fiction literature, television, and film – have changed the world in ways that go far beyond day-to-day gadgets and devices.

Big Problem – Big Solution – Big Impact

When you go to the grocery store and pick an item off the shelf – or better yet, select the product online for personal same-day delivery – we bet you will never encounter the name of Norman Borlaug.

He may not have had the direct inspiration of a science fiction author the same way that physicist Leo Szilard had, but what he accomplished is certainly within the spirit of science fiction thinking as we describe it in this book. Borlaug had a visionary perspective on technology and what it could accomplish, and imagined its impact on a much grander scale than the boundaries of the Midwestern farm states hit by the Dust Bowl in the 1930's. And that is one of the bigger lessons in his work: it is the thought process, the ability to imagine a future and find the way to make it reality, that underpins the approach we describe in this book.

Imagining the future of food (Goals #2, #12, and #15)

Three of the UN Goals for Sustainable Development reflect the desire to meet universal human need: access to an adequate supply of healthy food. Goal #2 (Hunger), Goal #12 (Responsible Production), and Goal #15 (Life on Land) are not only interrelated. They are also the same three goals which Norman Borlaug decided to pursue – and partially achieved on a global scale – over 80 years ago. He eventually became known as "the man who saved a billion lives." [71]

His quest began as he tried to understand the causes behind the Dust Bowl in the Midwestern United States in the 1930's, a catastrophic event which is considered "one of the worst environmental disasters of the Twentieth Century anywhere in the world" due to a combination of "drought and poor land use practice." [72] The severity of the crisis forced up to 400,000 people to move from the Midwest to California, "a significant population transfer in any era." [73] Born in 1914 and raised in Iowa, Borlaug experienced the effects of the Dust Bowl first hand. In his study of the causes and effects, he learned that the prevailing theory in the spirit of "poor land use" was that the Dust Bowl resulted from "excessive technological resources" applied to agriculture. Borlaug thought the opposite, that the Dust Bowl "… was actually the result of insufficient application of technology. He noticed that in places where techniques of high yield agriculture were being systematically applied, Dust Bowl conditions never developed with the same severity." [74] This thesis became a driving force behind what turned into a "decades-long, science-based international agriculture improvement and educational efforts" around the world. [75] Starting with what became known as the Mexican wheat program, Borlaug and his team became so successful that he has gone down in history as the "father of the Green Revolution". His work earned him the 1970 Nobel Peace Prize and he is only one of seven people to win a Nobel Prize and receive both the US Congressional Gold Medal and Presidential Medal of Freedom (joining, among others, Dr. Martin Luther King, Jr., Nelson Mandela, Mother Teresa, and Elie Wiesel). [76] [77]

Borlaug's legendary accomplishments fit clearly into the framework of "Big Problem - Big Solution - Big Impacts" context. In the spirit of innovation with purpose, his work prompted former US President Jimmy Carter (himself a former farmer) to issue this statement on Borlaug's 90th birthday: "For fifty-two years, Dr. Norman Borlaug has been helping to provide more food to the neediest areas of the world. But perhaps of greater importance, this distinguished scientist-philosopher has been demonstrating practical ways to give people of the entire world a higher quality of life." [78]

The impact of Borlaug's Green Revolution has not always been viewed as positive. It also begs the question of where world hunger and agriculture stand in 2018. Critics claim that Borlaug's work "displaced smaller farmers, encouraged overreliance on chemicals, and paved the way for greater corporate control of agriculture." [79] These conclusions also justify the need for the application of science fiction thinking to a problem as complex as world hunger. It is naive to think that there is a "free lunch" in the process of improving agriculture yields and encouraging responsible farming. The challenge is to find approaches which lead to a net positive impact, while working to mitigate the consequences.

This is a vital perspective, because it prevents the ideas generated by science fiction from decaying into a purely dystopian outcome. We are not denying that some of the solutions proposed under science fiction thinking – if left unchecked or unmitigated – could give rise to the dystopian visions which underpin many books and movies. To reiterate, technology is agnostic. John F. Kennedy echoed this sentiment with a veiled warning in a May 1961 speech: "Space science, like nuclear science and all technologies, has no conscience of its own. Whether it will become a force for good or ill depends on man." [80] Science fiction thinking provides a means to imagine and talk about the impacts.

Imagining the future of jobs

When you return to the grocery store once again and pick an item off the shelf – or better yet, select the product online for personal same-day delivery – we bet you will never encounter the name of Edward Bellamy.

Yet the means for paying for these purchases – a small plastic card – can trace its roots as far back as 1888. That was the year that Bellamy published his best-selling utopian novel Looking Backward, which involves a citizen of Boston who awakens in the year 2000, over 100 years after Bellamy's time. [81] In other words, debit and credit cards originally appeared in science fiction. It took several decades before credit cards established themselves, starting with Diners' Club and American Express in the 1950's. The debit card was a different kind of breakthrough, because in contrast to the credit card, it withdrew money directly and almost immediately from the cardholder's account. It was virtually bounce proof, and would eliminate the significant risks which banks, customers, and businesses faced with the use of cash or credit cards. One could even theorize about a cashless society. This makes the debit card in particular another science fiction idea originally from science fiction which fits the "big problem – big solution – big impact" framework.

Goal #8 on the Global Goals for Sustainable Development is "Decent Work and Economic Growth". The two are inextricably linked and delicately balanced, which only reinforces the need for science fiction thinking. We would reframe the question above as "how do we innovate for purpose and achieve exponential growth in a way that also creates jobs and minimizes the social consequences of that growth?"

The same McKinsey report echoes conclusions we presented in our book SAP Next-Gen: Innovation with Purpose, in which we emphasized our support for Goal #4 (Quality Education) and Goal #9 ("Industry, Innovation, and Infrastructure")

"If history is any guide, we could also expect that 8 to 9 percent of 2030 labor demand will be in new types of occupations that have not existed before. [Our] analyses lead us to conclude that, with sufficient economic growth, innovation, and investment, there can be enough new job creation to offset the impact of automation, although in some advanced economies additional investments will be needed as per our step-up scenario to reduce the risk of job shortages."

The idea of education itself is undergoing a transformation, and some of those changes have their roots in science fiction as well. One name we can associate with the transformation is Jill Watson a tutor at Georgia Tech University in Atlanta. Georgia Tech did an experiment with online tutors, and asked students in one class to rate their tutor experience along criteria including helpfulness, friendliness, and how approachable the tutor was. Watson ranked highest but had an even more special distinction. Jill Watson was not a human. She was the machine interface with a face, a background, and other mannerisms so well-crafted that there was no way to tell it wasn't a person.[82] [83] [84] The existence of Jill Watson recalls Her and similar movies.

Imagining the future of food and the future of jobs are daunting but necessary challenges. As Norman Borlaug himself said in a television interview in 2003: "Producing food for 6.2 billion people ... is not simple." [85]
There is no clear direct path yet from today's world to the achievement of these goals. How do we launch a collective effort to lead us from the simple but powerful expression of these goals to a world in which we have eradicated the problems which underlie them? How long will it take and what resources will the world need to harness?

We feel that these goals' complexity and scope, as well as the amount of time and resources needed to solve them, offer the ultimate challenge to our imagination. Science fiction thinking gives us a means to fill in the blanks, to formulate and answer the questions we need along the way. We can only master these challenges when we learn to place ourselves well into the future, maybe 10 years, maybe 50 years. Science fiction thinking allows us to imagine these problems as solved, then work our way back along many paths – technological, social, financial, political – to devise a way to achieve that goal while understanding the impacts, both positive and negative.

The "big problem" definition starts with the headline description of the Global Goals shown in Figure 3, but as we will see in the additional examples below, the "big solution" can take many forms, but these are irrelevant without an accompanying exploration of the impacts. Anticipating and hopefully mitigating these impacts creates the opportunity for an even better solution, with the highest net benefit to mankind.

Imagining the future of water

The amount of water withdrawn daily is mind-boggling. In the United States alone, withdrawals from freshwater, salt water and groundwater resources are estimated at 322 billion gallons per day, according to the government's US Geological Survey.[86] Almost 72 percent of those withdrawals go to only two uses: thermoelectric power and irrigation.

The gap between supply and demand for water is equally mind-boggling. In its 2015 report *Water for a Sustainable World*, the United Nations projected a global water deficit of 40 percent by 2030, assuming a "business as usual" scenario.[87] The challenge of course – in line with Goal #6 (Clean Water and Sanitation) – is to alter "business as usual" practices so dramatically that the world can collectively close that gap.

That is easier said than done. The World Economic Forum calls water "the ultimate systems challenge. It is a unique resource that underpins all drivers of growth – be it agricultural production, energy generation, industry or manufacturing. It also connects these sectors into a broader economic system that must balance social development and environmental interests."[88] The water challenge is much different depending on where a person lives. The UN declares access to safe drinking water and sanitation as a "human right, yet its limited realization throughout the world often has disproportionate impacts on the poor and on women and children in particular."[89] The report estimates that "748 million people lack access to an improved drinking water source, while billions more lack drinking water that is truly safe."[90]

In the United States, meanwhile, short-term and long-term threats have begun to emerge. Also, in 2015, a team of scientists from NASA, Cornell University and Columbia University forecast that the Western US faces its worst drought in 1,000 years. One NASA scientist said that water demand "has passed supply in some areas. Throwing 30 years of drought on top of that means we're going to have to change the way we live out here."[91]

One bold step in this process of addressing the projected 40-percent water gap and breaking with business-as-usual came in 2018, when SAP Next-Gen teamed with Startupbootcamp AfriTech, the World Economic Forum's Global Water Initiative, and World Bank's Water Global Practice to accelerate the search for solutions. The Epic Groundwater Challenge is a collaboration which aims to scale groundwater assessment solutions in emerging economies by discovering disruptive startups and innovative approaches, working with public and private stakeholders.[92]

According to Philip Kiracofe, CEO and co-founder at Startupbootcamp AfriTech, "Water resource management is a critical challenge of our time, and we believe startups can play a key role in developing disruptive solutions."

The aim of this initiative is to launch scalable and sustainable solutions through lean pilot engagements with sponsors. Follow-up phases of the initiative aim to globally scale the solution concepts.[93]

These are among the terrestrial challenges related to water. Reliable access to water will also be essential to the success of permanent installations or colonization of Mars. This is not as far-fetched as one might think. NASA has the goal of "boots on Mars" by the 2030s.[94] Prior to that, NASA plans to send the Europa Clipper to orbit Jupiter's moon Europa, which may contain a vast ocean under its icy surface. The Hubble Telescope has also found evidence that Europa's larger sister moon, Ganymede, may harbor a "subterranean ocean ... thought to have more water than all the water on Earth's surface."[95]

We can only begin to think of how these missions may encourage further space exploration and colonization, with the side effect of producing solutions which can help us solve problems on Earth. Many questions arise as we think about Europa and Ganymede: how do we get a team there? How do they drill through kilometers of ice? How do we ensure the quality of the water? How can we turn the water into fuel?

In the spirit of the Global Goals, the mission itself may not matter as much as the means and the mindset we need to complete it. In fact, it is hard for us to imagine a greater challenge for Innovation 4.0 and science fiction thinking than the future of water, in the short term here on Earth, and in the long term, beyond it throughout the solar system.

Imagining the future of cities

It is hard to imagine the future of cities in isolation. While one of the UN Goals addresses the future cities directly (#11 – Sustainable Cities and Communities), we see the solutions for this goal linked with other goals. Prominent on that list is not only water, as we discussed in the previous section, but also Goal #13, which is Climate Action.

To weave together a scenario which involves all three goals, let's transport ourselves 50 years into the future. If we wake up in the city of Chicago, what do we find? *Chicago Magazine* explored that very question in 2018 in an article called "The Shape of Water," which examines what will happen to the city of Chicago as major coastal cities in the US become flooded and people need to flee to a more livable place.[96] In one scenario in the article, Amazon ultimately decides to place its second headquarters in Chicago because it may be the only remaining livable large city in the United States, in part because it is near the world's largest single accessible supply of fresh water, the Great Lakes system. Karen Weigert and Richard C. Longworth of the Chicago Council on Global Affairs argued in an appeal for Amazon to place its second corporate headquarters in Chicago: "If you think about climate as a risk factor, this [Chicago] is a thriving city that will be better than a lot of other places when it comes to climate change."[97]

The introduction in *Chicago Magazine* frames up one look at that future Chicago in 2068, with a population of 20 million people compared to just under 3 million today. Where will these people live? How can the city support them with food, water, and other basic needs? How will they get from Point A to Point B? And how will Chicago itself deal with the higher temperatures from global warming, even though it is not exposed to the same flooding risks as the major cities along the coasts? These questions are only a small set of the ones we could ask to start a "future back" discussion: solving the problem, working back to today, and assessing the impacts, both positive and negative.

This discussion is fascinating because Chicago has existed for 150 years. But what if we ask the same questions about a city that does not even exist yet? What if someone takes the original core idea of Disney's Experimental Prototype Community of Tomorrow (EPCOT) and really creates an incubator for ideas for urban living?

That megacity is already on the drawing board in Saudi Arabia.

Called Neom – a combination of "neo" and the first letter of the Arabic word for "future" – the megacity would be larger than the country of Qatar and would be a "civilizational leap for humanity [98] Neom's website touts the project as "the world's most ambitious project: an entire new land, purpose-built for a new way of living." [99] The vision of Neom is to make it "the land of the future, where the greatest minds and the best talents are empowered to embody pioneering ideas and exceed boundaries in a world inspired by imagination."

In Neom, "[e]verything that can be automated will be" in a "hub between Europe, Asia and Africa, and a home drawing in people with the skills to create world-class businesses in industries from biotechnology to food." [100] The cost of stamping the megacity into the desert sands in the northern part of the Saudi Arabia is currently pegged at $500 billion from public and private investment. [101]

How long will it take to create Neom, and will the city succeed? Even skeptics have some hint of optimism in their comments. One critical voice seemed to describe Neom more as a mindset than a megacity, and wrote that Neom "may live up to only a portion of its promise, but if it galvanizes creativity and innovation, if it provides a more hopeful model for the future of the Middle East, away from oil and religious conflict and towards urban solutions infused with the best of technology, then it won't matter if it fulfills all of its dreams." [102]

Imagining the future of health care

The World Economic Forum (WEF) recently posed a question which elaborates in Global Goal #3 (Good Health and Well-Being): "How can we make a difference to the lives of billions suffering from neurological disorders, diabetes, heart failure, lung disease and cancer?"

Its own answer to the question draws a direct link between science fiction thinking and health care technology, and hints at the vast potential these technologies offer. "Technologies that were once the staple of science fiction movies are rapidly becoming realities." [103] One area where scientists and engineers have already achieved a science fiction to fact success is prosthetics.

Faced with the challenges of coming up with body suits, artificial limbs, or prosthetics, today's younger people could be forgiven if their first thoughts turn to Tony Stark and Stark Industries. After all, Tony Stark's alter ego, Iron Man, appeared most recently in the movie *Avengers: Infinity War*, which took only 48 days in the summer of 2018 to gross $2 billion at the box office.[104] Before making his way to the screen, Iron Man has been thrilling Marvel Comics readers since the 1960's.

So you can imagine the surprise back in 2015 when Robert Downey, Jr., the actor who portrays Tony Stark and Iron Man in the Marvel Comics movies, presented a 7-year-old boy named Alex Pring with a 3D-printed prosthetic arm of his own.[105] Prosthetics of the kind Alex needed normally cost around $40,000, but the total bill of materials for Alex's new limb came to a mere $350! [106]

How is that possible? The brains and heart behind that project is not the superhero Tony Stark, but rather a PhD student at the University of Central Florida (UCF) named Albert Manero. He and his friends – including mechanical, aerospace and computer engineers, a nurse, a seamstress, and advisers – worked feverishly over eight weeks in the UCF Machine Labs to create what 7-year-old Alex refers to as his "cool robo arm".[107] Manero is now president of

Limbitless Solutions, a non-profit organization which uses technologies such as 3D printing to manufacture personalized bionics and solutions for disabilities for children.[108] In 2018 the company announced the release of its latest bionic arm, adding finger movements as well as sleeves for children to personalize their limbs.

Limbitless Solutions is the first company to combine 3D printing with electromyography – an established technology that records the electrical activity of muscle tissue — to create a prosthetic arm for kids.[109] The company is now preparing clinical trials to obtain Food and Drug Administration (FDA) approval for the prosthetics and thus gain the ability to have insurance cover the costs.[110] Other more heavily funded projects are taking this *Iron Man* thinking about prosthetics to another level. Imagine a day when someone can control a prosthetic limb with their thoughts, the same humans control their natural limbs? Teams at Johns Hopkins University's Applied Physics Lab are literally taking some of the wildest science-fiction ideas – thought control and bionics – and merging them to improve people's lives. With the experimental Modular Prosthetic Limb, the teams are currently testing a person's ability to control a prosthetic arm and hand directly via electrode brain implants. The project is also testing the ability to restore touch sensation.[111] This project – as well as the highly flexible LUKE Arm now produced commercially by Mobius Bionics – has been funded since 2006 through a $120 million from a program run by the US Defense Department's Defense Advanced Research Projects Agency (DARPA) to help wounded warriors.[112]

As the question from the World Economic Forum at the outset of this section implies, bionics and mind-controlled prosthetics are only a small part of the global challenges in health care. We feel we are at the dawn of an age when Innovation 4.0 and the mantra of "big products – big solutions – big impacts" will turn many more science fiction ideas into fact in the health care field.

Chapter 5

✦ Activation starts with the simple needs

We are convinced that there is a science fiction imagination within every person. This thinking is now entering the corporate world, where science fiction thinking is becoming a mindset and a powerful enterprise tool to accelerate purpose-driven, transformative innovation in the spirit of the UN's Global Goals. In this final chapter of Part 1, we will endeavor to help you take a few steps within your own enterprise, startup, or your personal life.

We would encourage you to think about what you have read so far in our book and use it to activate your own science fiction imagination. We would also like to reinforce that this science fiction thinking is no longer a fringe activity or an ad hoc process for coming up with new ideas. The time has come for what we used to call "crazy" to become commonplace in business, a standard approach for finding big solutions to big problems while being keenly aware of all the major impacts they will have on society.

Anyone can do it!

Your entrée into the world of Innovation 4.0 begins when you activate that science fiction imagination within yourself. Achieving that comfort level, and emboldening others to speak up with their own seemingly wild ideas, is vital to the success of Innovation 4.0.

As we have witnessed with all the examples so far in our book, "crazy" is what built the world we live in and enjoy today, for all the challenges it may still have. With the convergence of imagination and 21st century technologies – from machine learning, blockchain technology, artificial intelligence, and augmented and virtual reality, to robotics, drones, the Internet of Things (IoT), and cloud technology – "crazy" will build our world faster than ever before, triggering exponential growth opportunities which also demand conscious management and care.

One tenet of the science fiction methodology is working "from the future back." Admittedly, the futures described in so many science fiction films are not always desirable ones. Many are filled with the dark imagery of dystopian worlds, in which leaders or rogues have applied technologies to fulfill corrupt purposes or evil intentions. If we took films such as James Cameron's *Terminator* literally, it means we are only a decade away from a post-apocalyptic world which resulted after an AI-based defense network launched a nuclear war.

"From the future back" or similar mantras are not meant to be inspirational posters. There is actually a methodology behind it that can help science fiction as we know appeal even to people who are not fans of the genre. When people empathize with the challenges people in the future may face and how they may overcome them, the approach can be constructive and useful. It can foster real change in mindset, and great ideas can come out of it.

Yes, people may think that science fiction is scary. The future can even be scary in a business context. Asking publishers to look 10 years into the future and imagine a world without printed books can be a frightening premise for a discussion. Our earlier example of the impact of plastic money on human bank tellers present many challenges for banks to anticipate and address. Science fiction tends to extend that timeline out even further than that, asking people to project 20-30 years into the future or perhaps all the way out to the year 2100.

But when we focus on the positives – cool things we want to have, cool ways we want to live – science fiction thinking can also be exhilarating. It is the tool which allows us not only to imagine, but also start creating the future of food, jobs, water, cities, climate, and health care. When we work with a grander purpose in mind, the exhilaration can become even stronger. Like any new technology, what we see portrayed in science fiction can have a dark side and good side. There is a utopian and a dystopian side to this, and too often the movies get into the dystopian side of things. That may make for thrilling entertainment, but it does not imply that these dark futures are unavoidable. In fact, it is just the opposite. We need to figure out how to greatly enhance the "good" in the outcomes of science fiction and mitigate the "bad" with similar intensity.

We like to think that when you use science fiction to build the future, you do it with purpose. The task can start with one central question: What problem are we solving? Maslow's Hierarchy of Needs offers a way to focus that question.

Figure 7: Maslow's Hierarchy of Needs [113]

The needs at the two bottom levels of the pyramid have much in common with the UN Global Goals. The message is that despite all our ongoing technological progress, the world still faces considerable challenges in basics such as food, water, employment, and health. That is why we need to imagine the future of food, the future of jobs, the future of water, and the future of health care as we did in Chapter 4.

Thanks to 21st century technologies and the right mindset, what is now changing is the way enterprises, startups, students, governments and citizens can pursue ideas which fulfill these needs. Our message is that during this new process, it is necessary to confront unintended consequences and negative impacts head-on rather than dismiss them. What fascinates us – and what should motivate enterprises, startups, governments, students, and citizens– is that anyone is capable of this thinking.

Getting comfortable with science fiction thinking in a corporate world

The irony is that until recently it has proven difficult to embrace science fiction thinking at work, but we do it subconsciously every day in our own homes. It is strange that for some reason we have not yet adapted as fast in corporate life as we are in our private lives.

Science fiction also remains a popular motif for page-turning thrillers and Hollywood movies. As we mentioned in Chapter 4, the latest Avengers movie needed roughly a month and a half to achieve $2 billion in ticket sales worldwide. We can also witness the success of the novel *Ready Player One's* movie adaptation, which grossed over $500 million worldwide in 2018.[114] Solo, the latest entry in the Star Wars canon, was the top-grossing film over the 2018 Memorial Day weekend in the United States, with box office revenues of $85 million.[115] This underscores the appetite the public has for entertainment which falls under the science fiction umbrella.[116]

On the television side, the *zeitgeist* around science fiction has led to original programming such as *Black Mirror*. The show examines modern society, particularly with respect to the unanticipated impacts of new technologies.[117] Episodes are standalone, usually set in an alternative present or the near future, often with a dark and satirical tone.[118]

But science fiction plays a much more important and vital role in our lives than merely serving as the setting and plot driver for entertainment. For centuries, science fiction has served as humanity's crystal ball, with remarkable clarity and accuracy. Many of the products, services, or experiences first encountered in these fictional worlds are now so interwoven in our daily lives that we take them for granted and forget their origins.

Enabling technologies and great ideas are changing the world so quickly right now that we can no longer afford this status quo, i.e. this gap between how we view science fiction professionally and how we view it privately. There is too much at stake. Science fiction thinking is powerful, but how do you reconcile having a "crazy" mindset in a corporate world?

One of our challenges is to help companies create their own science fiction gravity. To do that, we could have convened creative collaborators like science fiction writers, illustrators, designers, etc. But in this book, we are going to convene with a broader audience. This is a fully democratized process.

In our introduction we mentioned that science fiction thinking does not necessarily require technological or scientific skills, despite the presence of "science" in the name. The "how" is important, but not to the extent of the "what" and the "why". This is particularly true when we make the imagination of the impacts a fundamental part of the innovation process. It may sound easy to adopt that perspective, but experience shows that you can't flick a switch and make it happens solely from the technology side. This difficulty is what makes science fiction thinking a management challenge. Bill Buxton, a researcher at Microsoft, said that "the people who have the tech skills may not have the cultural and social skills. It's only when you get all those skills together that you get the perfect storm for the next breakthrough."

Steve Jobs echoed this comment when he said: "[T]echnology alone is not enough—it's technology married with liberal arts, married with the humanities, that yields us the results that make our heart sing." [119]

Let's take this one step further: anyone who ever thought "wow, if only ..." and let their imagination run wild can think this stuff up!

This has a powerful social angle too. What's going to be the impact in how we live? Everybody has a voice, everybody can bring in their ideas. The barriers to entry are intentionally low, but once again, that does not imply that the work is easy once you have entered the SAP Next-Gen science fiction to fact universe.

Everyone has ideas. A mindset of "beyond tomorrow" can foster more ideas, many of which may be doable and even scalable.

Ultimately, we are trying to make Innovation 4.0 a normality. Rather than going *"oh, all this new technologies and ideas, I don't totally get it so I'm not going to do anything about it"*, the Innovation 4.0 and science fiction thinking mindsets focus on opportunities: with all these new technologies and ideas, how can I use them to benefit me, my family, my company, my world? "Turtling" is not an option. This kind of structured approach to innovation – in effect, your membership in the science fiction thinking community – is a way to cope with the furious pace of technological change rather than become indecisive or paralyzed by it. It is for everybody. Everybody can participate, everybody can contribute.

"Life will be better when ... "

In the introduction we also said that each of us is capable of science fiction thinking. More specifically than saying that we all have the requisite imagination to be science fiction thinkers, we argue that every one of us has at some point wondered how "life could be better if only..." We will make that thought bolder and more assertive by phrasing it as "life will be better when ..." We ask you to transport yourself deep into the future and remember what you like while you are there. Then you start mapping the path which connects that remembered future to today.

When we ask you to do this, we are not expecting you to write a novel or a short story upon your "return." You don't need to aspire to become H.G. Wells (*The World Set Free*), Isaac Asimov (*I, Robot*), Neal Stephenson (*Snow Crash*), William Gibson (*Neuromancer*), or Ernest Cline (*Ready Player One*). This is ultimately a creative business exercise, not a literary one. All we are asking you to do is take a step back and fill in that blank in "life will be better when ..." That is one way to bring you into the right mindset, from which you can use science fiction thinking as a tool to innovate for a better future.

As you start to trace what connects the future to today – trying to work from the future back – the output of your science fiction thinking can be a design, a prototype, or even a business plan which renders what the world could look like along a longer time horizon. All of these can describe or encapsulate how you or your company can make that future come about. The gatherings we hold weekly under the "SAP Next-Gen science fiction Wednesdays" banner at our Hudson Yards office in New York City often have that result. Participants listen to a story or talk from a subject matter expert or receive a challenging future problem to think about. The goal of each individual or group is to deliver a first idea on what that solution could look like and just as importantly, what its impact could be.

If the goal is to fill in the blank for "Life will be better when ...." science fiction thinking serves as a methodology that helps develop the habit of optimizing for a better future. We intentionally draw a distinction here between a better future and a better present. Beyond the risk of projecting oneself into a dystopia, optimizing for a better present assumes that one works with the opportunities of the present. This is a natural inclination, manifested in conservative clichés such as "a bird in the hand is worth two in the bush." It is hard to dislodge this natural risk aversion. In other words, it is easier and more natural for us to plan for and grasp what is in the immediate or near future, but this draws our attention away from greater and – dare we say it – crazier opportunities.

One reason we need to be bold in our solutions and projections is that the positive impact must clearly and unequivocally outweigh the negative consequences. Behavioral psychologist Daniel Kahneman and his academic partner Amos Tversky developed what they called prospect theory, which means that if the positive and negative impacts we experience from an event have an equal magnitude, the overall perceived impact will be negative.[120] In other words, people have a natural inborn tendency to feel the pain of a loss more than they feel the thrill of a gain. Kahneman won the 2002 Nobel Prize in economics for this theory.

To put it bluntly: this is why you need to be "positively bold" in your visions of the future under science fiction thinking. It is better and in fact necessary to push the boundaries of crazy rather than imposing limits or constraints on your thinking. "Crazy" is only a judgment from today's narrow perspective, the same perspective which science fiction thinking encourages – or dare we say it – compels you to transport yourself into that better world, envision all of the impacts (financial, commercial, cultural, political, and social) and then work your way back to the present, even if the tether to today is thin and tenable.

How crazy is crazy? Don't worry about that answer!

This is how Arthur C. Clarke described the gray areas and the tensions inherent in what we call "science fiction thinking":

"Trying to predict the future is a discouraging and hazardous occupation, because the prophet invariably falls between two stools. If his predications sound at all reasonable, you can be quite sure that in 20 or at most 50 years, the progress of science and technology have made him seem ridiculously conservative. On the other hand, if by some miracle, a prophet could describe the future exactly as it was going to take place, his prediction would sound so absurd, so farfetched, that everyone would laugh him to scorn."

"This has proven to be true in the past, and it would undoubtedly be even more so in the century to come. The only thing we can be sure of in the future is that it will be absolutely fantastic. So if what I say now seems to you to be very reasonable, then I'll have failed completely. Only if what I tell you appears absolutely unbelievable, have we any chance of visualizing the future as it really will happen." [121]

The point is that none of those boundaries is an absolute. Anyone can push those limits as they see fit, or better said, develop and tell a story that can't help but push those boundaries.

Pushing the limits of boldness also has another connotation. While it is easier and perhaps more entertaining to imagine a dystopian outcome to science fiction thinking, the flipside is the idea of a utopian outcome. How desirable is a utopian outcome? Sir Thomas More first coined the term in 1516 in his work *Utopia*, which described a perfect society on an island in the Atlantic Ocean. Without diving to deeply into More's work, one takeaway is that More wrote *Utopia* as a satire, as if to point fun at the very notion of the "perfect place".

In the context of SAP Next-Gen Science Fiction Thinking, we would argue that a perfect world is neither achievable nor desirable. For one thing, it would be boring and mean the end of progress. Nothing will ever change, there's no way to gain any kind of advantage, or make anything better. In other words, it extinguishes the fire that drives the "Life will be better when ..." motivation.

This is also the kind of thinking which is accessible to anyone. All you need is some imagination, a heart, and some critical thinking. We can all form an opinion on the goals and how to achieve them, even if we have never seen a *Star Wars* movie or a *Star Trek* episode or read lots of science fiction. We also hope these examples encourage you to think in even bolder terms about solutions, without ridicule. Remember that the degree of crazy doesn't matter if you keep pushing the limits with some link to the present, no matter how tenuous.

Are you activated? Welcome to the SAP Next-Gen Science Fiction Universe!

Get ready to explore.

PART 2

The SAP Next-Gen science fiction to fact universe

"I would argue until I'm blue in the face that science fiction is the quintessence of being human in a sense. We are technological beings. We are the only truly conscious species that we know of."

– James Cameron [122]

Immerse in the "what", "why" and "how" of the future

In the early 1980's, renowned science fiction author Isaac Asimov told an audience at a small college about how people give him credit for the many items he "invented" in his books. They gave him credit for inventing the hand-held calculator, he laughed, citing just one example. But Asimov admitted that while he could describe its appearance and purpose of the calculator – the "what" and the "why" – he had "absolutely no idea what was inside the thing! I had no idea how it would work." [123]

The hand-held calculator may not strike anyone as a "disruptive technology" in a world where billions of people use their smartphones for hours every day. But in its era, that device resulted in behavioral shifts which changed established cultural norms. People currently younger than 50 years old probably have absolutely no idea that "when solid-state electronic calculators first came on the scene in the 1960's, they revolutionized the way we learn and work." [124]

The imagining of a combination of "what" and "why" – initially independent of the "how" – is another way to characterize the essence of science fiction thinking. But the challenge is: how do you get to the "what" and the "why", once you have the desire because you have activated your inner science fiction passion and immersed in the future? What steps does an enterprise or an individual undertake so that it can practice Innovation 4.0 and make science fiction thinking a normality?

The poet Kirpal Singh, an associate professor of English literature at Singapore Management University, feels strongly that "science fiction should be compulsory teaching in schools. Nations with the best science fiction – America, Poland, the Nordic countries – are doing very well today in terms of emotional and ideological adjustments to the new technological era," he added. "[C]ountries such as Singapore tend to be mostly apprehensive and thus afraid of tomorrow." [125]

What today's business practices mean in a science fiction context

If we wanted to find one short phrase which sums up the genesis of 21st century life we would say "fiction to fact". If you're going to keep up with the pace of change, you've got to start thinking along these "fiction to fact" lines. You can't just eke your way forward or focus on incremental innovation. One way to do that is to completely rethink today's business practices. When you work from the future back, your perspective on processes will certainly change. We could say that this perspective gives you an advance preview of *tomorrow's* business practices. Think of it this way: a business practice based on 20 years of experience is wonderful and valuable. But in today's rapidly changing technological environment – when we assume that anything is possible – isn't the enterprise better served by business practices which incorporate the promise of the future, and not merely adhere to the norms of the past? This is another benefit derived from looking 20 or more years into the future and working back to today.

Those are the opportunities which people such as James Cameron and Isaac Asimov and countless others have provided us. They inspire us to travel through time, explore and understand what we see, then return to today with a chance to build that better tomorrow or get a "do over" to correct or avoid the things which may have gone awry.

That transition truly has created the world we live in. When we started to explore technological breakthroughs of today and through history, we noticed a pattern and a common thread. They have been designed, conceived, and realized by people who either grew up with science fiction, were inspired by science fiction, or just had a vision which they might not have called science fiction, but would have been considered as such as if they'd written a book or produced a movie instead of inventing a product, new business model or concept.

Why create a SAP Next-Gen Science Fiction Universe?

As SAP Next-Gen worked more and more with science fiction thinking, we realized that a links exists between science fiction books and movies and futuristic thinking in business. That led us to conclude that science fiction thinking is not only a powerful enterprise tool, but one that also could benefit from additional focus, awareness, and resources. It needs to be a system, not just a greater number of ad hoc events. Companies that will survive and thrive are those that will innovate at a pace equal to or faster than the rate of change in technology and society, while avoiding the fear and apprehension that the poet Singh referred to.

That means leaders can no longer plan around old models and traditionally derived practices or emphasize near-term optimization. They must accelerate their innovative capacity by designing new products and services, and craft the social and business models for a future that cannot be clearly perceived at present. Creating a sustainable culture using Innovation 4.0 requires not merely effort or focus, but immersion in four areas: [126]

- **Mindset:**
  How is the individual going to change his or her own perspective? How will people activate their imaginations and sustain that new mindset?

- **Skill set:**
  How do leaders ensure that access to and development of capabilities takes place across the entire enterprise?

- **Knowledge set:**
  What insights is the enterprise gathering from its sojourns into the future? How is it disseminating those insights, preserving them, and using them to their advantage?

- **Tool set:**
  What methods, approaches, and techniques are available to teams and individuals to make change happen and stick?

Culture is the overarching element. To make an organization "future ready," the culture needs to encourage people to bring their science fiction mindset to work, and dare to imagine bold ideas rather than incremental improvements. The engineering and infrastructure advisory firm Aurecon refers to this idea as being "future ready." Maureen Thurston, global director for Design to Innovate at engineering and infrastructure advisory firm Aurecon, stresses the hard work required for being future ready, and how some people confuse the trappings of the future – in the form of a one-off foray into design thinking or some background reading – as being sufficient.[127]

"Hiring a 'design thinking' consultant, running a few workshops, swapping sticky notes, or reading a blog or two will not miraculously produce a culture of innovation," she says.
"It takes forward thinking leadership, a long-term investment strategy, and a lot of dedicated effort. It is – in fact – very hard to do."[128]

To establish that culture, leaders need a process they can trust as well as sources to draw on for inspiration. Just as science fiction itself takes on many forms, we believe that businesspeople need many entrée points to the science fiction mindset. There is no single, specific path to success, beyond remaining true to the Innovation 4.0 equation and the idea of "big problems – big solutions – big impacts."

The futurist Alvin Toffler published his landmark book *Future Shock* in 1970. Among the many points in his book, two remarks remain just as compelling today as when Toffler wrote them almost 50 years ago.

"It is safe to say that, unless specific countermeasures are taken, if something can be done, someone, somewhere will do it," he asserted. "The nature of what can and will be done exceeds anything that man is as yet psychologically or morally prepared to live with."[129] The answer to how we develop those countermeasures and how we prepare ourselves to absorb the outcomes of these new technologies is science fiction thinking, as manifested in Innovation

4.0. Without that immersive input, supported by systematic guidance, we risk running headlong into that spectacular future without having assessed the impacts and consequences. Another remark by Toffler presaged that sentiment. "If we view [science fiction] as a kind of sociology of the future, rather than as literature, science fiction has immense value as a mind-stretching force for the creation of the habit of anticipation," Toffler wrote.[130] Then he made an appeal similar to Kirpal Singh's:

"Our children should be studying Arthur C. Clarke, William Tenn, Robert Heinlein, Ray Bradbury, and Robert Sheckley, not because these writers can tell about rocket ships and time machines, but more important, because they can lead young minds through an imaginative exploration of the jungle of political, social, psychological, and ethical issues that will confront these children as adults." [131]

Where should both children and adults turn for their inspiration? The sources are not always deadly serious or dystopian. Several years before video chat appeared in *2001: A Space Odyssey*, it was the standard form of communication in the animated television series *The Jetsons*, which first aired in 1962. The comics introduced us to something remarkably like the Apple Watch when Dick Tracy started using his two-way wrist communicator in 1946. Granted, the Apple Watch isn't atomically powered, but this article traces the progression of Detective Tracy's watch from fiction to fact.[132]

Other forms of popular culture have attempted to show us fictional worlds which have started to become fact or have served as crucibles for these ideas on their way from fiction to things we now take for granted. Think of the 1939 World's Fair in New York City, which among other things introduced millions of people to television (some thought it was a magic trick!). Other introductions which we now take for granted today included fluorescent lights and nylon. That fair even hosted what is considered the first world science fiction convention, called Nycon 1.[133]

Think of the "Imagineering" teams which plan and build the rides and exhibits at the Walt Disney parks throughout the world. Disney himself conceived of the Experimental Prototype Community of Tomorrow (EPCOT) in the 1950's.[134]

The creative well produced by science fiction thinking is an extraordinary tool to facilitate business thought processes and to design the processes themselves. Science fiction creatives are not constrained by the ideas of technological and social innovations based on the present state. And by now, we hope you have realized that you are also a science fiction "creative"! Hand in hand with the ideation phase of design thinking, they expand the universe of possible innovations and their applications. By pushing imaginations to their limits, businesses can find a competitive edge in simultaneously innovating more rapidly and innovating with purpose. Not only can the business keep up with the future's rapid onslaught, but it can also fundamentally form some of that future as well. The key is to immerse in science fiction thinking to build a culture ready to pursue Innovation 4.0.

In a popular sense, science fiction holds our attention because it shows us the cool things we want to have, and the cool ways we want to lead our lives. Let's look into the future and find more of these cool things and lifestyles and leave the potential for dystopia and dire consequences aside for a moment and think again of all the wonderful changes to our lives which originated in science fiction.

Entering the Sci-Fi Universe

In this chapter we will immerse ourselves into the major parts of the SAP Next-Gen Sci-Fi Universe, which we described briefly and showed graphically in our introductory chapter. We reiterate that image here as Figure 8.

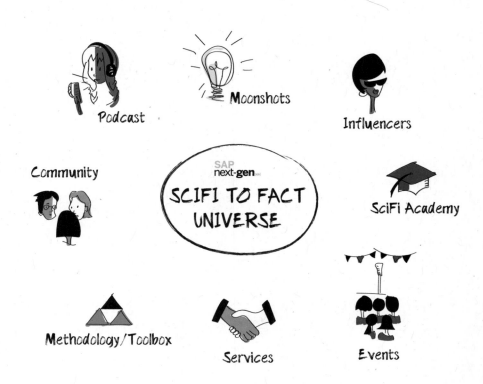

Figure 8: The SAP Next-Gen Sci-Fi to Fact Universe

Methodology/Toolbox:

Innovation 4.0 and science fiction thinking are actual operational frameworks designed to turn science-fiction-to-fact from an accidental or ad hoc process into something which is commonplace within the 21st century enterprise. Science fiction thinking combined with design thinking gives you a tool box which accelerates the impact of purpose driven innovations, helped by a mindset of a time traveler who looks back from the future and sees the actions needed to achieve a purposeful outcome. When incorporating purpose into our thinking, we suggest linking to one or more of the UN Global Goals, which you can learn about at globalgoals.org/business.

Figure 9 below illustrates the components of science fiction thinking.

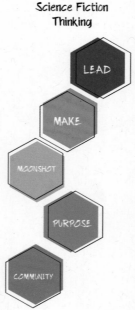

Figure 9: Science Fiction Thinking Components

Infusing the process with the "why" question inspires a team to think bigger and bolder, to focus on solutions with exponential growth potential, and to understand the broader impact of the solution. Some companies have already adopted approaches along these lines, including what Moog, Inc. calls "scenario-based planning." Retired US Air Force colonel James A. Regenor, Founder, Blockchain Resources Group, elaborated on that process for us.

"We use scenario-based planning, in which we'll try to paint a picture of what the future looks like, imagine ourselves in that future, and then we'll do a 'right-to-left' methodology," he said.[135] The "right to left" methodology is what we have referred to throughout the book as "working from the future back" instead of projecting the present into the future.

Regenor used the example of a journey to Mars to make his point. If someone stands on Earth and tries to figure out how to get to Mars, the task can seem overwhelmingly complex and daunting, if not impossible. But if someone stands on Mars, looks back at Earth, and asks "how did we get here?" the perspective changes. You accept *ex ante* that the "what" is possible and you work backwards to today to figure out the "how."

"The hardest bias to overcome is folks who say, 'that's not possible'," Regenor said, reinforcing the need to take people on a journey into the future, then work "right to left" across time.

Brian David Johnson, a futurist at the leading chip maker Intel, also stresses the importance of science fiction as a means to build that sturdy bridge from the future back to today. "We control our own future," he writes in his book *Science Fiction Prototyping: Designing the Future with Science Fiction*. "It is precisely because of this that we must talk about the future we want to live in and explore the various futures we must avoid. Science fiction gives us a language so that we may have a conversation about the future."[136]

In Chapter 3, when we explored the roots and psychology of science fiction thinking, we stressed that science fiction thinking needs to maintain a tether to today's reality, regardless of how thin or tenuous that link may be. This provides additional reassurance that it is in fact possible and desirable to work from the future back and connect to today. Along that journey, the enterprise can ask itself what role it can play, what technologies it can contribute, and why its participation is important.

The new paradigm of science fiction thinking transforms not only the enterprise, but also the individual. Collective immersion enables and empowers the company, while the team member benefits from the immersion as well. Figure 10 shows this progression, color-coded to correspond to the steps in the science fiction thinking framework in Figure 9.

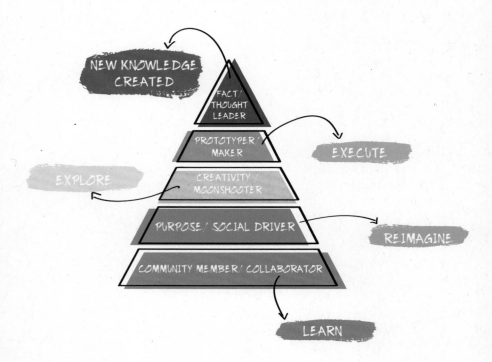

Figure 10: The individual develops herself or himself as well, as the immersion in science fiction thinking progresses.

You can start your science fiction learning journey by joining the community. You may already be an ardent fan of science fiction movies or books but have not yet applied that same passion to your professional life. Or you may be someone who has little working familiarity with *Star Wars* or *Star Trek*, never mind some of the classic authors, futurists, moviemakers, artists, or designers whose works inspired the world we inhabit today. Or you may be somewhere in between these extremes. No matter what, the process starts with learning. We hope this book has already given you a rich, varied, and deep head-start to your learning process.

Think back to the comments of Maureen Thurston, though. As she implied, reading a blog or two, or dabbling in science fiction in some form, is a necessary first step, but by no means the last step in the development process. The next step is the discovery of a purpose, a direction, and making a commitment to it. We emphasize again that the United Nation's Global Goals for Sustainable Development offer a clear and compelling set of purposes to start that journey. In Chapter 4 we showed how individuals – from startups, citizens, students to universities to large corporations to governments – have begun to pursue these goals by imagining the futures of food, jobs, water, cities, and health care, and then building those futures.

Once someone has become a Purpose Driver, the next step is the Moonshot, in line with the third step in the science fiction thinking process. A Moonshooter not only explores his or her own imagination to its limits, but also challenges others to do the same. Later in this chapter we will have a separate section on Moonshots.

At this point, you have reached a level of skill in the "what" and "why" parts of the process. Sitting squarely amid a richly rendered and desirable future, the natural next step is to ask, "how did we get here?"

"How" is not only a technical question. It is also a political, social, ethical, and commercial question. This is the moment when executing on the maximum power of science fiction thinking truly comes to the forefront. We imagine a fully-formed, detailed future so that we can explore and understand both the positive and negative impacts. Progressing further, the time comes to start making that thinking a reality. The Prototyper may be putting together an actual physical prop or rendering, or maybe a video or a story, or vision to allow others to travel through time along the innovation path you laid out. The Prototyper pushes us toward "how" and "fact."

The incentives to reach the top of the pyramid, where new knowledge is created, should be incredibly strong. Whether it is the desire to solve a global problem, change the lives of millions or even billions of people, make a fortune, or all three, the leaders – many of whom are the influencers we mentioned earlier – are never finished with their work. For them, the process starts over again, which is why you see people such as Richard Branson turning their attention to several problems in parallel.

The journey up this pyramid is an exhilarating experience. Most people who join the community may never achieve the status of our influencers, but at the same time the opportunities to change the world in the spirit of Innovation 4.0 are limitless. To reiterate a point, we made in the book *SAP Next-Gen: Innovate with Purpose*, the world is not running out of big ideas, nor will it ever.

Moonshots

How far do you want to let your imagination go? Moonshot ideas bend the boundaries of our imaginations without breaking them. Throughout history, the boldest visions have often been the ones which gave teams the intense focus and enduring energy to make the seemingly impossible come true.

X (formerly Google X) is built around the idea of moonshots. As Astro Teller explains: "Generally, we think of moonshots this way: The first is, there has to be a huge problem with the world that we want to solve. The second is that there has to be some science-fiction sounding product or service that, if we could make it, however unlikely that is, it would make that problem go away. And then there has to be some technology breakthrough that gives us some faith that we could actually at least get started on trying to build that product or service".[137]

That description echoes one of the defining moments of the 20th century.

Imagine a young, charismatic leader imploring his or her nation to put its money and its best minds into the largest peacetime initiative the nation has ever undertaken. The leader can paint a compelling picture of the "what" and "why" for that pursuit but has absolutely no idea about the "how". Would you follow?

To many of the nation's citizens, that initiative probably sounded like lunacy, true to the origins of that word.[138] Others may have dismissed the notion as "science fiction", implying that such schemes are more at home in Hollywood or on the pages of some dystopian thriller.

But that is the initiative which John F. Kennedy committed his nation to during his first year in office. Read how Kennedy outlined the mission in his landmark speech at Rice University in Houston, Texas on May 25, 1961.

"But if I were to say, my fellow citizens, that we shall send to the moon, 240,000 miles away from the control station in Houston, a giant rocket more than 300 feet tall, the length of this football field, made of new metal alloys, <u>some of which have not yet been invented</u>, capable of standing heat and stresses several times more than have ever been experienced, fitted together with a precision better than the finest watch, carrying all the equipment needed for propulsion, guidance, control, communications, food and survival, <u>on an untried mission, to an unknown celestial body</u>, and then return it safely to earth, re-entering the atmosphere at speeds of over 25,000 miles per hour, causing heat about half that of the temperature of the sun—almost as hot as it is here today—and <u>do all this, and do it right, and do it first before this decade is out</u>—then we must be bold." [139]

The realities first revealed to us in science fiction need not be as bold as a pioneering journey to the moon or as unsettling as the dystopian setting in so many movies and novels. President Kennedy had no idea how the moonshot was going to happen. He had no technical understanding of the required science and engineering. But once he professed the goal, it became aspirational and then transformative. Contrary to what we normally think about the term science fiction, Kennedy did not need to write a book or produce a film to lend plausibility to the idea. He just needed to plant the seed with a few minutes during a speech.

One primary goal of this book and the entire SAP Next-Gen science fiction to fact universe is to help you plant your own seeds, and then reap the harvest. The fascinating and true thing about Kennedy's dramatic moonshot and Asimov's now-obsolete calculator is that each one of us is capable of such moments. Each of us can conceive a product, a service, or a concept that solves a problem, perhaps ultimately for millions of people. That process often involves examining our own needs, or own pressing problems, and imagining the "what" and "why" that can eliminate them. Even if we don't describe or depict the invention in detail, we certainly can perceive and perhaps articulate the positive feelings it evokes.

And while we will emphasize big global problems in this book, the calculator story also shows that there are small-ticket products that can emerge from the context of science fiction thinking and still elicit enormous behavioral changes. That is one of the main points of this book. The spectrum of ideas associated with science fiction is vast. It ranges from household items to atomic energy and rocket science. Channeled and harnessed in the way we describe in this book, science fiction thinking is a powerful means to come up with inspiration and even visionary business plans to explore what President Kennedy once called "the unknown, the unanswered, and the unfinished." We find a positive solution which also mitigates the effects of disruptive change on those whose current lives are displaced.

Pushing the limits was implied in Kennedy's moonshot speech in May 1961, when he said that the United States will "choose to go to the moon in this decade, and do the other things, not because they are easy, but because they are hard." [140] He added that the goal will serve to "organize and measure the best of our energies and skills."

SAP Next-Gen science fiction academy

The SAP Next-Gen science fiction academy is made available for the SAP Next-Gen community which includes academic thought leaders and researchers, students, startups, accelerators, tech community partners, SAP customers, purpose driven partners and institutions, etc. The SAP Next-Gen community leverages 3,700+ educational institutions in 117 countries, 130+ SAP Next-Gen labs/hubs at universities and at partner and SAP locations, 100+ SAP Next-Gen Chapters, 25+ innovation communities through a partnership with Startup Guide, a growing global network of 40+ Girls' Lounges in a partnership with The Female Quotient, as well as startups, accelerators, tech community partners, venture firms, futurists, and purpose driven institutions. The community also leverages SAP's 100+ innovation, development and customer experience centers and SAP's network of 17,000+ partner companies.

The SAP Next-Gen SciFi academy offers opportunities for the community to activate their science fiction mindset through events such as meetups, boot camps, and festivals where they can apply the latest technologies and methodologies to specific problems. We hold these events around the world. One of the major events is the annual SAP Next-Gen Festival for the SDGs, where faculty learn how to bring science fiction thinking to their students, enabling them to boldly reimagine their worlds without limiting themselves with the constraints of yesterday's technologies. Thinking like a science fiction visionary can set the stage for an individual's purpose-driven digital innovation journey, and later the same journey within an enterprise as the students collaborate (through hackathons, etc.) or work directly with a company.

Community

The SAP Next-Gen science fiction community is part of the above mentioned SAP Next-Gen community which goes across 116 countries and includes universities, SAP Next-Gen Labs, SAP Next-Gen Chapters, etc.

Community has multiple meanings in our context. On the one hand, it embraces all the people who have made an entrée into the Universe. Another aspect is how these people communicate and exchange ideas, taking full advantage of social media, crowdsourcing opportunities, or face-to-face meetings.

The SAP Next-Gen science fiction community uses science fiction thinking to boldly envision the intelligent enterprise and create disruptive and purposeful innovation. Industry partners can picture their intelligent enterprise empowered with machine learning, blockchain technology, artificial intelligence, augmented and virtual reality, robotics, drones, the IoT, and cloud technology. They can envision a future where the 17 UN Global Goals are realized, based on the enabling technologies which help us render the what, why, and how.

The SAP Next-Gen science fiction community also enables unique interactions among some of the most influential futurists. You will find creatives and performing artists, inventors, authors, movie producers, C-suite executives and industry experts, brand marketers, media agencies, venture capitalists, academics, entrepreneurs and aspiring entrepreneurs, and digital influencers.

Events

We conduct organized events around the world, from meetups to festivals to conferences, to bring people together in an environment that both intensifies and celebrates their immersion in science fiction thinking. On a smaller scale, we offer our regular SAP Next-Gen Sci-Fi Wednesdays at SAP Hudson Yards in New York City. With the larger festivals, panels, and conferences around the world, we facilitate or support events which allow community members to engage with each other directly and activate their science fiction mindset. Like-minded futurists gather to hear the latest on science fiction to fact and to absorb the latest on how today's digital disrupters are embracing science fiction thinking. They can envision their own futures and those of their enterprises and industries.

Among the important events in 2018 were our SAP Next-Gen science fiction festivals. We also launched SAP Next-Gen for voice at Voice Con in May 2018, bringing a focus onto how voice interaction will be a key driver for accelerating Innovation 4.0. Here we cite only one of many possible examples of how voice is already serving the UN Goals, in particular Goal #3 (good health and well-being). By 2020, according to studies [141], half of all searches will be initiated by voice, and voice and smart speakers are expected to penetrate 55%

of U.S. households by 2022. An article in *Harvard Business Review* said that this situation "is no different for physicians. In a nationwide survey of pediatricians conducted by Boston Children's Hospital (not yet published), 62% of respondents said they have used voice-assistant technology, and one-third own, and use, at least one 'smart speaker.'" [142]

The events are also a showcase for the creativity and influence that can be unlocked by science fiction thinkers. One such thinker is Ciara Judge, founder of Germinaid Innovations. In the spirit of "big problems – big solutions – big impact" she used bacteria found naturally in soil to increase crop productivity by up to 74 percent, a level which could help solve the global food crisis. What makes this story particularly compelling is Ciara's age.

She founded Germinaid when she was 15.

Ciara is a champion for why businesses should invest in youth to solve big challenges. Since founding Germinaid she and her teammates have won numerous awards, including the European Union Contest for Young Scientists and the Google Global Science Fair, for their research on the work of rhizobium with cereal crops. In September 2014, *Time Magazine* named Ciara as one of the 25 most influential teens worldwide. [143]

Influencers

Whose lives are in one way or another an embodiment or manifestation of science fiction thinking? That list could be quite long, dating back to the pioneering authors in the 1800's. Fast forward to the 21st century, and we can list entrepreneurs such as Richard Branson (Virgin) and Astro Teller (X) as well as futurists such as Ray Kurzweil, entrepreneurial journalists such as Berit Anderson, and explorers and film directors such as James Cameron. We would also include the late novelists Octavia Butler and Arthur C. Clarke.

They have all served as thought leaders and evangelists for science fiction thinking, because they have experienced first-hand how science fiction can inspire people to transform their imagination into reality.

Services

One important example of our services under the umbrella of SAP Next-Gen is our boot camps for science fiction thinking with enterprises. One piece of feedback in particular from one of these workshops in 2018 underscores how effective and inspiring these approaches can be: "SciFi thinking as a creative tool has made me dream again."

Cross-functional teams activate their science fiction thinking and then use a range of interactive techniques to apply it to a problem aligned with one or more of the UN Global Goals that their enterprise could help solve. By transporting participants anywhere from 10 to 50 years into the future, we start to imagine solutions to these problems and go through the process of working "from the future back". Teams can finish the day with an initial business plan or even a prototype of a solution. No matter what the form of the output is, they finish the day inspired to continue the search for big solutions to big problems.

The following two examples demonstrate that science fiction thinking is becoming a mindset and a powerful enterprise tool to accelerate purpose-driven, transformative innovation. The dawn of Innovation 4.0 has arrived, and the appetite for the new perspectives it opens is growing.

Let's look first at financial services. Major financial companies face rapid change thanks to the enabling technologies we have cited in this book. Imagine a world in which machine-learning investment algorithms can personalize a customer's investment portfolio, or where blockchain is restructuring monetary systems via cryptocurrencies. These have suddenly become two of the immediate challenges these institutions face. They are no longer in the realm of futurists and dreamers. At the same time, financial services groups need to think about what kind of social and economic impact these developments will have.

For one major European financial services group, the SAP Next-Gen Boot Camp on science fiction thinking activated a team of innovators. These leaders are expecting major changes and disruptions to their industry in the near future, and within 20 years the changes may be so dramatic that they upset economic foundations that have persisted for hundreds of years.

The boot camp "brings your mindset way out of the box," one participant said. "Now my head is full of ideas about how the company must and can innovate for the future." The innovators left the boot camp loaded with ideas that could very well guide them through the disruptive futures they know are coming.

The second example relates directly to Goal #3 (good health and well-being) and indirectly to Goal #8 (decent work and economic growth). As you have read a few times already, science fiction is rapidly becoming science fact in the realm of medicine, with more futuristic ideas on the way. After an SAP Next-Gen Boot Camp on science fiction thinking with about 45 colleagues, a director of a major health care enterprise said that "taking a sci-fi mindset really allowed us to open up our minds and think differently about the possibility of healthcare – what that means here in the United States – and how we should position ourselves as an organization to get to that interesting, creative and sustainable model."

One of the teams at the boot camp envisioned new additional jobs at their company in the next 10 to 15 years. The team saw a clear role for a behavioral specialist/psychologist who would help individuals who neglect to take care of themselves. These specialists would rely on various at-home, highly personalized medical services to encourage and incentivize patients to participate in treatments. This new link between the company and patients would improve the quality of health care and at the same time make the company more efficient and profitable.

Podcast

Our podcasts help community members stay up-to-date on the many facets of science fiction thinking, including the latest ideas and success stories. They can hear the latest insights on using science fiction thinking to stretch beyond limitations, reimagine the future of industries, and envision the actions needed for a future when the 17 UN Global Goals are realized. We invite you to join our podcast series.

sapnextgensciencefiction.podbean.com

The SAP Next-Gen science fiction to fact universe continues to expand. More approaches, ideas, and above all, more purpose-driven innovators – including corporate executives, startup founders, visionaries leading accelerators, academic thought leaders, researchers and students, purpose driven innovation evangelists at institutions and non-profits, and citizens – are immersing themselves every day in a science fiction thinking mindset. By getting this far in our book, you are already in the community. Now is the time to take your next steps.

Chapter 8

How SAP Next-Gen is turning science fiction into fact

In addition to the SAP Next-Gen science fiction to fact universe, we are working with many enterprises who are pursuing Innovation 4.0. SAP Next-Gen methodologies have helped them envision, plan, and implement the kinds of bold solutions we have described so far in the book. Many of those solutions have a direct link to one or more of the UN Global Goals.

As we draw close to the end of this book, we would like to share additional examples of how science fiction has inspired the science facts of today.

In the 1968 movie "2001: A Space Odyssey" a voice-interactive sentient computer called "HAL" is able to control systems which affect the environment on-board a space vessel. Today's voice interactive devices like Amazon Alexa and other smart assistants are given increasing control of the home and corporate environments, all through voice responsive interactions.

The 1898 science fiction novel "War of the Worlds" by H.G. Wells inspired Robert H. Goddard in his development of the liquid fuel rocket which ushered in the space age. Recognizing his pioneering work in rocketry, NASA named its first space flight complex after him: the Goddard Space Flight Center.

In the film, "Hitchhiker's Guide to Galaxy" 2005, a special fish-like organism known as Babelfish was able to enter the ear of a person and translate any language in the galaxy. Sounds like fiction? In fact, today we see multiple products from companies like Waverly Labs, Google, and TimeKettle that offer real-time translation earbuds.

In "Back to the Future Part II" 1989, protagonist Marty McFly famously puts on a pair of shoes which automatically lace. In 2016, Nike created a real-life version of this self-lacing power shoe, called HyperAdapt, a product that can now be purchased online. We conclude the book with additional examples that highlight how SAP solutions support customers in a variety of industries from around the world, with the stories all told in terms of "big problems – big solutions – big impacts."

⚬ Power to the people: Banking in Latin America ¹⁴⁴

Millions of people in rural Latin America lack bank accounts. They are forced to rely on riskier ways to manage their money. Driven by compassion and hope, one bank is changing that, using mobile technology from SAP.

Big problem:
Working for cash, "the unbanked" in Latin America are more vulnerable to theft. They can't establish a credit history, so it is impossible to secure bank loans for cash shortages or investments. How can a bank help break this cycle and improve the lives of people? This is the question that Compartamos asked Mother Teresa. Her response? "Look after them."

The bank is doing exactly that, with help from SAP.

Big Solution:
Compartamos was quickly able to make a difference by becoming a "customer-shaped bank" which offers microloans to budding entrepreneurs, particularly women. But they also had a much bigger goal – to eradicate financial exclusion – so they needed help from SAP.

Together, they planned to reach people where they live, often traveling to remote communities. The next step was to help the people adopt unfamiliar digital technology.

Now, supported by SAP mobile solutions, customers can bank from anywhere using their smart phones. The bank's customer base is growing rapidly, and the bank continues to offer new services, thanks to reliable and scalable technology from SAP.

Big Impact:
When no longer "unbanked", millions of people stand a better chance to break the cycle of poverty. By taking care of the unbanked, Compartamos and SAP are following the advice given by Mother Teresa – and helping make the world a better place.

Turning air into opportunities: Wind power [145]

The planet is in dire need of sustainable energy, yet only a small percentage of global electricity comes from wind power. A major wind turbine company is working with SAP to help power-up that percentage.

Big problem:
Wind turbines are often installed in remote areas under harsh conditions. Complex planning is done onsite and can change daily, based on weather and supplies. Plans are painstakingly drawn up on whiteboards or paper. Communication can be challenging. All this complexity is reflected in the cost of labor and crane rentals. Together, SAP and Vestas, a pioneer in wind energy and hybrid solutions, took up the challenge to streamline the process and reduce costs.

Big Solution:
The goal was to make wind energy even more cost-effective for worldwide customers. SAP and Vestas resolved to create a digital tool that would standardize onsite planning and provide access to data – in real-time – for construction managers, technicians, subcontractors, customers, and suppliers, 24 hours a day, wherever they are. And it had to be easy, so busy workers could focus on what they do best.

Big Impact:
With the same information available to everyone – from construction managers to customers – Vestas is now streamlining projects, delivering faster, more efficient, and more cost-effective wind turbine installation, and bringing clean and sustainable energy to the world more quickly.

◌ Data-drive harvests: Food in Brazil [148]

Hundreds of millions of people are living in hunger. Now, a progressive agricultural equipment manufacturer has teamed with SAP to address the future of the world's food supply.

Big problem:
Today, the planet has 7.6 billion people to feed. By 2030, there could be 2 billion more. Farmers, under pressure to produce on a larger scale, need a better way to increase yields. How can agribusinesses produce enough to feed the world's exponentially growing population in an efficient and sustainable way?

Big Solution:
Stara was the first Brazilian company to equip agricultural machinery with SAP Leonardo internet of things (IoT) technology and achieve a "data-driven harvest." This has truly revolutionized their business. With a platform connected to the cloud, farmers can now monitor vital farming processes. They can collect real-time data about planting, soil preparation, fertilizing, harvesting, and more – allowing them to better manage their farms. And with real-time data at their fingertips, they can determine the exact amount of fertilizer to apply in each section of farmland.

Big Impact:
The result was increased productivity, the right amount of fertilizer used, and sustainable farming. Projected at a larger scale, the solution developed by Stara and SAP could have an enormous impact on the world food supply by enabling the intelligent feeding of the world. By contributing to sustainable farming, there are benefits all around – for farmers, the planet, undernourished people, and future generations.

Building responsible supply chains: Ethical sourcing [147]

Businesses may be assuming more risk than they realize by using suppliers that engage in unethical business practices. There are ways to gain insight into the complete supply chain – and minimize risk.

Big problem:

Could a company unknowingly facilitate child or forced labor? Is a company violating environmental protection rules? Is it bypassing sustainability best practices? Today's best-run businesses are no longer rubber-stamping a supplier's choice of low-cost country locations. They're relying on insights, traceability, and visibility from SAP Ariba to eliminate uncertainties and potential risks. How do businesses know if there are disreputable or even illegal practices lurking in their supply chains?

Big Solution:

The SAP Ariba Supplier Risk with Sustainability solution can help build ethical supply chains – leveraging Ariba Network and using key technologies such as SAP HANA. Aggregating more than 600,000 data sources in over 130 risk types, the solution employs data science to customize signals for each customer. It also provides risk scores and alerts specific to their region and category.

Monitoring forced labor risks is a key component of the offering. With alerts in place, businesses can zero in on possible violations and take action to ensure ethical practices – and the protection of human rights – in every link of their supply chains.

Big Impact:

With transparent and sustainable supply chains, businesses around the world can help safeguard human rights as well as the environment. And because "doing good" is also good business, companies can contribute to a strong global economy while protecting their own brand reputations and profitability.

Science fiction has been a tantalizing form of entertainment and inspiration on the fringes of our world for a couple of centuries. What we are beginning to recognize and acknowledge is that insights from science fiction were part of creating the world we live in today. As the pace of technological progress increases so rapidly that we now live in an "anything's possible" world, now more than ever we need the kind of conscience, foresight, and inspiration that can come from science fiction thinking linked to purposeful outcomes.

This is the basis of Innovation 4.0 and a vital ingredient for enterprises and individuals who want to innovate with purpose and tackle the 17 United Nations Goals for Sustainable Development.

In the spirit of rapid technological innovation, we already see the first glimpses of Innovation 4.0 on the horizon as shown in Figure 11. They combine the UN Global Goals for Sustainable Development with exponential technology and science fiction thinking to inspire purposeful innovation in the intelligent enterprise. We invite you to join the SAP Next-Gen Science Fiction Universe, activate your inner science fiction mindset, and be part of the movement to achieve the UN Global Goals by 2030.

Welcome to Innovation 4.0!

Figure 11: Innovation 4.0

REFERENCES

[1] https://www.smithsonianmag.com/science-nature/ten-inventions-i 1 nspired-by-science-fiction-128080674/

[2] https://www.washingtonpost.com/news/the-switch/wp/2017/04/19/how-to-build-your-own-moonshot-labaccording-to-astro-teller/?utm_term=.c5ef1092c497

[3] https://hbr.org/2017/07/why-business-leaders-need-to-read-more-science-fiction

[4] https://www.smithsonianmag.com/science-nature/ten-inventions-inspired-by-science-fiction-128080674/

[5] https://genesismission.jpl.nasa.gov/people/biographies/goddard.pdf

[6] Ibid

[7] https://www.bcg.com/en-us/publications/2018/business-opportunity-solving-world-big-problems.aspx

[8] https://www.un.org/press/en/2018/sga1817.doc.htm

[9] Nayak, P. Ranganath and Ketteringham, John M, Breakthroughs! How the Vision and Drive of Innovatorsin 16 Companies Created Commercial Breakthroughs That Swept the World, Rawson Associates, 1986

[10] Ibid, pp. 154-155

[11] https://www.tor.com/2018/04/27/five-stories-that-celebrate-the-everyday-in-science-fiction/

[12] https://www.cnbc.com/2017/05/08/amazon-jeff-bezos-artificial-intelligence-ai-golden-age.html

[13] Interview with Gerrit Roessler, March 2018

[14] https://www.nytimes.com/2018/03/30/movies/hal-2001-a-space-odyssey-voice-douglas-rain.html

[15] Comments made at the MusicBiz 2018 conference in Nashville, TN

[16] https://www.statista.com/statistics/274774/forecast-of-mobile-phone-users-worldwide/

[17] Nayak, P. Ranganath and Ketteringham, John M, Breakthroughs! How the Vision and Drive of Innivators in 16 Companies Created Commercial Breakthroughs That Swept the World, Rawson Associates, 1986

[18] https://www.aps.org/publications/apsnews/201510/physicshistory.cfm

[19] https://www.nytimes.com/2008/02/10/opinion/10cox.html?ex=1360299600&en=9ef4be-7de32e4b53&ei=5090&partner=rs-suserland&emc=rss&pagewanted=all&_r=0

[20] http://news.bbc.co.uk/2/hi/uk/2963619.stm

[21] https://www.telegraph.co.uk/technology/blackberry/11347347/The-history-of-BlackBerry-inpictures.html?image=2

[22] https://www.wired.com/story/guide-iphone/

[23] https://www2.deloitte.com/content/dam/Deloitte/us/Documents/technology-media-telecommunications/us-global-mobile-consumer-survey-second-edition.pdf

[24] https://www.imdb.com/title/tt0060397/

[25] https://www.proteus.com/

[26] https://www.fda.gov/newsevents/newsroom/pressannouncements/ucm584933.htm

[27] https://www.theverge.com/2017/11/14/16648166/fda-digital-pill-abilify-otsuka-proteus

[28] https://psychnews.psychiatryonline.org/doi/full/10.1176/appi.pn.2017.pp12a2

[29] https://www.nytimes.com/2016/02/17/technology/virtual-reality-companies-look-to-science-fiction-fortheir-next-play.html

[30] https://hbr.org/2017/07/why-business-leaders-need-to-read-more-science-fiction

[31] 2016, http://www.popsci.com/swallow-pill-to-monitor-your-vitals

[32] New Scientist https://www.newscientist.com/article/2144050-tiny-robots-crawl-through-mousess-tomach-to-heal-ulcers/

[33] http://www.ehang.com/ehang184/

[34] https://www.cbsnews.com/news/flying-car-blackfly-developers-give-first-look-cbs-this-morning/

[35] https://www.zdnet.com/article/dubais-autonomous-flying-taxis-a-reality-in-2018/

[36] https://www.audi-mediacenter.com/en/press-releases/audi-supports-air-taxi-project-in-ingolstadt-10375

[37] https://www.audi-mediacenter.com/en/press-releases/audi-italdesign-and-airbus-combine-self-drivingcar-and-passenger-drone-9900

[38] https://www.entrepreneur.com/article/307278

39 https://www.smh.com.au/technology/a-drone-you-can-sit-inside-intel-showcases-air-taxi-to-avoid-roadtraffic-20180110-p4yyd4.html

40 https://www.zdnet.com/article/dubai-begins-testing-drone-taxi-service/

41 https://money.cnn.com/2018/02/08/technology/ehang-self-flying-drone/index.html

42 https://www.vtol-investor.com/blog/2018/6/21/derrick-xiong-

43 https://www.goldmansachs.com/insights/technology-driving-innovation/drones/

44 https://discover.sap.com/best-run/44 en-us/customer-Vectus/index.html

45 https://discover.sap.com/best-run/en-us/customer-Hakusan/index.html

46 Clarke, Arthur C., Profiles of the Future, originally published in 1962

47 https://www.theguardian.com/technology/2014/jun/09/what-is-the-alan-turing-test

48 http://www.hansonrobotics.com/robot/sophia/

49 https://news.un.org/en/story/2017/10/568292-un-robot-sophia-joins-meeting-artificial-intelligence-andsustainable

50 Ibid.

51 Ibid.

52 http://www.asia-pacific.undp.org/content/rbap/en/home/presscenter/pressreleases/2017/11/22/rbfsingapore.html

53 http://www.hansonrobotics.com/about/david-hanson/

54 World Economic Forum, 2015

55 World Economic Forum, 2015

56 https://www.weforum.org/agenda/2016/06/the-poetry-of-progress/

57 https://www.economist.com/special-report/1999/10/07/cutting-the-cord

58 https://hbr.org/2017/07/why-business-leaders-need-to-read-more-science-fiction

59 https://www.reuters.com/article/us-oil-bp/bp-sees-self-driving-electric-vehicles-crimping-oil-demandby-2040-idUSKCN1G41XK

60 https://www.technologyreview.com/s/534866/why-we-dont-have-battery-breakthroughs/

61 https://www.cnbc.com/2017/08/07/elon-musks-tesla-could-soon-be-overtaken-in-batteries-armsrace.html

62 http://www.chicagomag.com/Chicago-Magazine/April-2018/The-Future-of-Water/

63 Gabler, Neal, Walt Disney: The Triumph of The American Imagination, New York: Vintage Books, 2006, pp. 609-610

64 https://www.bloomberg.com/graphics/2017-neom-saudi-mega-city/

65 http://strangehorizons.com/non-fiction/articles/estrangement-and-cognition/

66 http://www.kurzweilai.net/dont-fear-artificial-intelligence-by-ray-kurzweil#!prettyPhoto

67 http://kalamu.com/neogriot/2013/07/09/history-octavia-butler-gave-us-a-few-rules-for-predicting-thefuture/

68 https://www.wired.com/2013/02/moonshots-matter-heres-how-to-make-them-happen/

69 https://www.cnbc.com/2018/05/22/spacex-president-gwynne-shotwell-wants-her-work-to-inspirewomen.html

70 https://www.smithsonianmag.com/science-nature/ten-inventions-inspired-by-science-fiction-128080674/

71 https://www.normanborlaug.org/index.html

72 http://ocp.ldeo.columbia.edu/72 res/div/ocp/drought/dust_storms.shtml

73 http://faculty.washington.edu/gregoryj/dust%20bowl%20migration.htm

74 http://www.agbioworld.org/biotech-info/topics/borlaug/special.html

75 https://borlaug.cfans.umn.edu/about-borlaug/significance

76 https://en.wikipedia.org/wiki/Norman_Borlaug

REFERENCES

[77] https://www.technologyreview.com/s/415334/norman-borlaug-agronomist-who-fought-world-hungerdies/

[78] http://www.agbioworld.org/biotech-info/topics/borlaug/quotes.html

[79] https://www.nytimes.com/2009/09/14/business/energy-environment/14borlaug.html?adxnnl=1&adxnnlx=1252954842-H/5SC9xrFT2pMOxCai5B1g&pagewanted=all

[80] https://er.jsc.nasa.gov/seh/ricetalk.htm

[81] https://www.nytimes.com/2011/12/04/magazine/the-cardboard-beginnings-of-the-credit-card.html

[82] https://www.sciencealert.com/this-college-used-an-ai-bot-as-teaching-assistant-and-none-of-the-studentsnoticed

[83] https://pe.gatech.edu/blog/meet-jill-watson-georgia-techs-first-ai-teaching-assistant

[84] https://www.washingtonpost.com/news/innovations/wp/2016/05/11/this-professor-stunned-his-studentswhen-he-revealed-the-secret-identity-of-his-teaching-assistant/?utm_term=.08e4c22f2eef

[85] https://www.technologyreview.com/s/409243/green-revolutionary/

[86] https://water.usgs.gov/watuse/wuto.html

[87] Water for A Sustainable World, The United Nations World Water Development Report 2015, p. 11

[88] https://www.weforum.org/projects/global-water-initiative

[89] Water for A Sustainable World, The United Nations World Water Development Report 2015, p. 3

[90] Ibid., p. 19

[91] https://news.nationalgeographic.com/news/2015/02/150212-megadrought-southwest-water-climateenvironment/?utm_source=Facebook&utm_medium=Social&utm_content=link_fb20150214newssuperdrought&utm_campaign=Content&sf7464928=1

[92] https://news.sap.com/2018/08/epic-groundwater-challenge-sap-next-gen-crowdsourcing-disruptive-ideas/

[93] Ibid.

[94] https://www.smithsonianmag.com/science-nature/inside-nasa-plan-send-humans-mars-180958787/

[95] https://sservi.nasa.gov/articles/nasas-hubble-observations-suggest-underground-ocean-on-jupiterslargest-moon/

[96] http://www.chicagomag.com/Chicago-Magazine/April-2018/The-Future-of-Water/

[97] http://www.chicagotribune.com/news/opinion/commentary/ct-perspec-amazon-bezos-hurricane-climatechange-0914-story.html

[98] https://www.bloomberg.com/graphics/2017-neom-saudi-mega-city/

[99] http://www.neom.com/

[100] https://www.economist.com/middle-east-and-africa/2017/10/26/saudi-arabia-launches-a-futuristiceconomic-zone

[101] https://www.reuters.com/article/us-saudi-arabia-reforms/klaus-kleinfeld-appointed-adviser-to-saudicrown-prince-maaal-idUSKBN1JT07K

[102] https://www.wired.com/story/saudi-prince-plans-a-city-of-the-future-dont-bet-on-it/

[103] https://www.weforum.org/agenda/2017/01/2017-is-the-year-healthcare-goes-sci-fi/

[104] https://www.businessinsider.com/movies-to-hit-2-billion-at-box-office-including-infinity-war-2018-6

[105] https://www.cnn.com/2015/03/12/health/robert-downey-jr-robotic-arm-irpt-feat/index.html

[106] https://blogs.microsoft.com/firehose/2015/02/18/the-collective-project-changing-the-world-with-bionicarms-for-kids/

[107] https://www.ucf.edu/pegasus/kid-approved/

[108] https://limbitless-solutions.org/about/

[109] https://www.orlandosentinel.com/health/os-ucf-limbitless-solutions-clinical-trial-20180514-story.html

[110] http://enablingthefuture.org/2018/05/30/limbitless-solutions-begin-clinical-trials-for-3d-printed-arms/

[111] https://www.darpa.mil/program/revolutionizing-prosthetics

[112] https://www.nytimes.com/2015/05/21/technology/a-bionic-approach-to-prosthetics-controlled-bythought.html

[113] Adapted from Maslow, Abraham H. A Theory of Human Motivation, originally published in 1943

[114] http://variety.com/2018/film/box-office/ready-player-one-500-million-steven-spielberg-1202778645/

[115] http://www.boxofficemojo.com/weekend/chart/

[116] https://www.theguardian.com/film/2018/may/29/han-solo-star-wars-story-falls-short-100m-us-takingsfranchise

[117] https://en.wikipedia.org/wiki/Post-industrial_society

[118] https://en.wikipedia.org/wiki/Alternate_history

[119] Cited in: https://hbr.org/2018/09/having-a-growth-mindset-makes-it-easier-to-develop-new-interests

[120] See Kahneman, Daniel and Tversky, Amos Choices, Values, and Frames, Cambridge University Press, 2000

[121] https://youtu.be/5UZS5vnnZl8

[122] https://www.indiewire.com/2018/04/james-cameron-science-fiction-amc-visionaries-1201958681/

[123] Account from someone who attended that talk at Wheaton College, Norton, MA

[124] http://www.keyelco.com/blog-details.cfm?blog_id=7

[125] https://www.straitstimes.com/lifestyle/arts/singapore-fantasy-fiction-takes-flight

[126] Adapted from: https://www.linkedin.com/pulse/how-thinking-like-designer-creates-value-maureen-thurston/

[127] https://www.linkedin.com/pulse/how-thinking-like-designer-creates-value-maureen-thurston/

[128] https://www.linkedin.com/pulse/how-thinking-like-designer-creates-value-maureen-thurston/

[129] Toffler, Alvin, Future Shock, New York: Bantam Books, 1970, paperback edition, p. 205

[130] Ibid., p. 425

[131] Ibid., p. 425

[132] http://techland.time.com/2013/02/11/dick-tracys-watch-the-most-indestructible-meme-in-techjournalism/

[133] https://en.wikipedia.org/wiki/1939_New_York_World%27s_Fair

[134] https://www.esquire.com/entertainment/news/a35104/walt-disney-epcot-history-city-of-tomorrow/

[135] https://www.youtube.com/watch?v=7CwtDfpQ_U4

[136] Johnson, Brian David, Science Fiction Prototyping: Designing the Future with Science Fiction, San Rafael, CA: Morgan & Claypool, 2011, p. 3

[137] https://www.washingtonpost.com/news/the-switch/wp/2017/04/19/how-to-build-your-own-moonshotlab-according-to-astro-teller/?utm_term=.c5ef1092c497

[138] Lunacy derives from the Latin word for moon, "luna" and the word "lunaticus", which means moonstruck. It referred to "intermittent periods of insanity, such as were believed to be triggered by the moon's cycle"; www.dictionary.com

[139] https://er.jsc.nasa.gov/seh/ricetalk.htm

[140] https://er.jsc.nasa.gov/seh/ricetalk.htm

[141] https://techcrunch.com/2017/11/08/voice-enabled-smart-speakers-to-reach-55-of-u-s-householdsby-2022-says-report/

[142] https://hbr.org/2018/03/what-will-health-care-look-like-once-smart-speakers-are-everywhere

[143] http://www.tedxteen.com/talks/changing-the-world-in-your-pajamas-ciara-judge

[144] https://discover.sap.com/best-run/en-us/customer-Compartamos/index.html

[145] https://discover.sap.com/best-run/en-us/customer-Vestas/index.html

[146] https://discover.sap.com/best-run/en-us/customer-stara/index.html

[147] https://discover.sap.com/best-run/en-us/customer-ariba/index.html